Lost-Wax Casting

Cover Photograph: Highly abstract anthropomorphic lost-wax casting from the Sinú Region, Colombia, South America -- Dated ca. 1000 CE
(Photo © Museu del Oro, Bogota, Colombia)

Lost-Wax Casting

Old, New, and Inexpensive Methods

Fred R. Sias, Jr., Ph.D.

Woodsmere Press
Pendleton, South Carolina

LOST-WAX CASTING:
OLD, NEW, AND INEXPENSIVE METHODS

Copyright © 2005 by Fred R. Sias, Jr., Ph.D.

Woodsmere Press
P.O. Box 726
Pendleton, South Carolina 29670-0726
www.woodsmerepress.com

Library of Congress Control Number: 2005908139

Publisher's Cataloging-in-Publication Data

    Sias, F. R. (Fred R.)
        Lost-wax casting: old, new, and inexpensive methods / by Fred R. Sias, Jr.
        -- 1st ed. -- Pendleton, SC : Woodsmere Press, c2005.
        xii, 202 p. : ill. ; cm.
        Includes bibliographic references and index.

        ISBN-13: 978-0-9679600-0-5 (pbk.)
        ISBN-10: 0-9679600-0-2 (pbk.)
        ISBN-13 978-0-9679600-1-2 (spiral)
        ISBN-10: 0-9679600-1-0 (spiral)

        1. Precision casting. 2. Molding (Founding). 3. Jewelry making. I. Title

TS233.S526 2005

739.27—dc22   2005908139

Dedication

Dedicated to the memory of my father, Ralph Sias, who taught me by example to be an inquiring engineer and a careful craftsman.

Acknowledgments

This book is the result of interaction with a number of persons. The late Cliff Wilson, then with Swest, Inc., was the first to give me ideas and hints that are not in the standard texts on lost-wax casting. Carl Schwartz, retired Research Director, Ransom and Randolph, suggested that I try a new burnout method. Tim Steeper taught me wax design. Paul Downing stressed the special requirements for designing castings to support and protect opals. Paulette Werger introduced me to Ashanti casting. Many students should receive credit for commenting on the rough drafts that were originally presented to them.

The illustrations have been obtained from various sources. I thank the Israel Antiquities Authority and the Museo del Oro, Bogota, Columbia. I especially thank The Contenti Company, Grobet USA, Kerr Lab, and Neytech for providing many illustrations from their catalogs to illustrate basic equipment required for lost-wax casting.

Several persons have reviewed the text at various stages of development and have offered useful suggestions. I thank Ann Brandt, Julia Van Deusen, Bob Jones, Carol Sues, Fred Ward, and expecially my sister, Peggy Lantz, who with the precise eye of an editor fine tuned the final drafts. Finally, I thank Dorris Sias for collaborating with me during my early adventures with lost-wax casting.

Table of Contents

Preface

This book is designed to be used both as a textbook and a reference book. It is directed primarily at beginners. Experienced casters, however, will probably find some useful ideas; they may even find some new techniques.

Heavy emphasis is placed upon understanding why things are done in a particular way, rather than simply presenting a set of cookbook rules that will always work. Sometimes understanding the scientific foundation for a particular technique makes it possible to simplify or shorten a step in the overall process.

Many of the ideas presented here are not original. I have listened to many experts to pick up hints and ideas that are included in the chapters that follow. I have had discussions with engineers and scientists at companies that produce the tools and supplies for lost-wax casting. I have picked up ideas from the Internet and have engaged in useful discussions with many others.

Sometimes experiments were performed to find out whether something would work or to determine the optimum time or temperature for an operation. Some of the methods presented will be quite different from the "usual" approach, but I have tried to

show the rationale for the alternative approach,
based either on scientific reasoning or practical
experiments.

I hope this book will be useful both to the craftsman
without much money as well as the technician in a
well-stocked shop. I have offered homemade solutions to many of the equipment problems for the
person on limited funds, as well as the reasons for
using more complicated or expensive pieces of
equipment.

If you are a neophyte I hope that this book will help
you get started in a fascinating craft; perhaps the
more experienced craftsman will find some new
ideas. I look forward to the discussion that some of
the ideas will stimulate.

6000 Years of Lost-Wax Casting

Lost-wax casting is an ancient art and craft. The first evidence of gold lost-wax casting is a small gold stud or "terminal" found in Syria and dated at 4200 BCE. A statuette of a female figure was among six cast objects found on the Amug Plain in North Syria. It was made around 4000 BCE.

The use of wax for making a model for casting seems to have originated at several locations around the world. While the most ancient evidence for this approach to metal working is found in the Middle East near the Tigris and Euphrates rivers in what is now Iraq, the process has been invented elsewhere in locations with no apparent contact with the Middle East.

Four hundred objects of bronze, ivory, and hematite were found in 1961 in a cave near Masada in Israel. The cache included crowns, standards, scepters, disks, horns, jars, mace heads, and tools. They were wrapped in a fiber mat and have been carbon dated to between 4000 and 3500 BCE. Many of the objects are lost-wax castings made of a bronze alloy of copper, antimony, and arsenic. Figure 1.1 is a picture of one of the crowns.

Figure 1.1
Bronze crown found near the Dead Sea in Israel Dated ca. 4000 BCE (Photo from the Collection of the Israel Antiquities Authority)

Ancient lost-wax bronze castings have been found at several locations in the Middle East and China. Egyptians used the lost-wax process to cast small copper parts before 2200 BCE. Gold lost-wax castings have been found in the tombs of Egypt.

The Chinese Bronze Age is considered to have extended through three dynasties: the Xia dynasty, the Shang dynasty, and the Zhou dynasty, from about 2000 BCE to 500 BCE. Unlike their western counterparts, Chinese artisans used clay piece molds to make ritual bronze vessels for most of this period and only adopted lost-wax techniques near the end of the Chinese Bronze Age.

By the time of the civilization of Classical Greece (600-500 BCE) the craft of lost-wax casting had developed to what are essentially the methods in use today. The head, arms, and feet of the famous bronze, "Charioteer of Delphi" (475-470 BCE), shown in Figure 1.2, were cast using lost-wax methods and attached to a torso that was cast separately. Evi-

Figure 1.2
The Charioteer of Delphi cast in ancient Greece using the lost-wax technique (Photo: ©2004 David Monniaux)

dence of twenty foundries has been found in the area around the ancient *agora* in Athens, Greece. The casting pits can be recognized by the masses of charcoal, lumps of metal and slag, and fragments of terra-cotta molds used in the casting process.

While one usually thinks of using the lost-wax process to cast relatively small objects and jewelry, the process is also used to cast very large bronze statues. The current techniques differ little from the methods used by the Greeks and Romans to produce statues, bronze doors, and other large objects. Only the details vary somewhat from current jewelry techniques. For example, ancient metalsmiths probably used terra cotta or clay instead of a plaster of Paris investment to produce their molds.

The Colossus of Rhodes, one of the Seven Wonders of the Ancient World, was a hollow bronze statue that stood 105 feet high at the entrance to the harbor at Rhodes in the Mediterranean Sea. It is said that the lost-wax process was used to cast the various parts of the statue. The statue stood for 65 years, from 290 to 225 BCE, until an earthquake toppled it. The wreckage lay undisturbed for eight centuries before it was salvaged and the bronze sold to merchants to be melted down and resold.

Lost-wax casting of precious metals must have evolved as soon as techniques in bronze were developed. There is little evidence of very early gold casting because gold is so easily melted and re-cast into more modern objects.

Tombs of the Pharaohs and early Greeks were regularly plundered; however, cast gold objects dating to hundreds of years before the Christian era have been found.

Pre-Columbian gold

Long before Columbus discovered the New World, native societies of Central and South America had perfected the art of casting gold objects using the lost-wax process. Gold lost-wax castings have been found preserved in Central and South America, even though tons of gold were melted down and shipped to Spain during the early sixteenth century. Figure 1.3 shows a gold casting from Colombia.

Figure 1.3
Lost-wax casting from Colombia, South America Dated ca. 1000 CE (Photo © Museu del Oro, Bogota, Colombia)

Goldsmiths in what is now Colombia may have invented the methods used in Central and South America. The earliest evidence of pre-Columbian lost-wax casting is usually dated around 1000 CE although recent finds indicate that the Moche in nearby Peru were accomplished metalsmiths by 400 CE and could have employed lost-wax casting techniques. The Chavin culture pre-dates the Moche and there is some evidence that Chavin metalsmiths produced lost-wax castings during the height of their culture between 800 and 200 BCE.

Ashanti bronze

On the Gold Coast of West Africa in present-day Nigeria, several past cultures have produced magnificent cast bronze sculptures. Lost-wax bronze casting methods were used by African metalsmiths some time after 1000 CE in Ife and Benin near the mouth of the Niger River in present-day Nigeria. The lost-wax bronze casting techniques were developed after an Iron Age period, and it is not clear whether the techniques evolved independently or were imported from Europe or elsewhere. The primitive lost-wax techniques are still in use today by descendants and are sometimes called Ashanti casting.

Historical Records

There are few records of the techniques used by ancient metalworkers. Some drawings on tomb walls or scenes drawn on ancient pottery depict general methods; however, the earliest detailed descriptions of cire perdue, or lost-wax casting, are the writings of Theophilus. While the exact date and even the true identity of the author is open to conjecture, three books were written around 1100 CE that described in great detail the techniques used by painters, glass makers, and metalworkers. Earlier written descriptions were generally sketchy and were sometimes written by historians not completely familiar with the technology being described. During the 1500s in Europe, lost-wax casting technology was well advanced. Much of what we know is from the writings of Georgius Agricola and Benvenuto Cellini. Their writings, listed in the references, are well worth reading to gain more historical perspective.

Modern technology

Dr. Taggert, a dentist, experimented with centrifugal casting to make gold tooth inlays in 1907. Early twentieth century dentists cast using centrifugal force by swinging a flask overhead on a chain. Finally centrifugal casting methods were adopted for manufacturing jewelry in 1940. Today, both centrifugal and vacuum methods are used to force metal into molds. Dental and jewelry-casting technicians share most of the modern investment-casting techniques.

References

Harry Jackson, *Lost Wax Bronze Casting*, Northland Press, Flagstaff, 1972.

Peter Northover, Email Communication, August 7, 1995. jpn@vax.ox.ac.uk

Dave Schneller, "The Cave of Treasures", *The Santa Fe Symposium on Jewelry Manufacturing Technology*, Met-Chem Research, Inc., Boulder, CO, 1988.

S. Shalev, and J. P. Northover, "The metallurgy of the Nahal Mishmar hoard reconsidered", *Archaeometry*, 35(1), 1993, 35-47.

Ian McNeil, *An Encyclopedia of the History of Technology*, Routledge, London, 1990.

The Metropolitan Museum of Art, *The Great Bronze Age of China*, Knopf, New York, 1980.

Carol Mattusch, *Greek Bronze Statuary,* Cornell University Press, Ithaca, NY, 1988.

J. M. Camp, *The Athenian Agora,* Thames & Hudson, Ltd., London, 1970.

Percy Knauth and Editors, *The Metalsmiths,* Time-Life Books, New York, 1974.

Pal Kelemen, *Medieval American Art,* Dover, New York, 1969, p 241.

National Geographic Society, *Wonders of the Ancient World: National Geographic Atlas of Archeology,* The National Geographic Society, Washington, DC, 1994, p 286.

Pierre Meauze, *African Art: Sculpture,* World Publishing Co., New York, 1968.

Denis Williams, *Icon and Image,* University Press, New York, 1974.

Theophilus Presbyter, *On Divers Arts,* (Translated from Latin by J. G. Hawthorne and C. S. Smith) Dover, New York, 1979.

H. C. Hoover and L. H. Hoover, De Re Metallica (translated from the first Latin Edition of 1556 by Georgius Agricola), Dover Publications, New York, 1950.

C. R. Ashbee, *The Treatises of Benvenuto Cellini on Goldsmithing and Sculpture,* Dover, New York, 1967.

Sharr Choate, *Creative Casting,* Crown Publishers, New York, 1986.

J. F. Jelenko & Co., *Crown and Bridge Construction,* A Handbook of Dental Laboratory Procedures, J. F. Jelenko & Co., Inc., New Rochelle, NY, 1968.

Six Steps for Casting

The Basic Concept

The lost-wax process is simple in concept. First, an object is modeled in wax. Wax rods or wires called *sprues*[1] (pronounced "sproos") are attached to the model, and the entire object and sprues are encased in a modified form of plaster of Paris called *investment*. The wax wires are left projecting from the investment and will later become the passageways through which metal enters the mold.

After the investment has solidified, the wax model, encased in plaster, is placed near a fire or in an oven to melt the wax. When the wax has all melted or vaporized, a cavity remains that may be filled with metal. The fact that the wax has disappeared of course leads to the term *lost-wax process*. The French term for the process is *cire perdue*, which literally means "wax lost" or "wax wasted."

1. Please see the Glossary for definitions of words unique to foundry work, lost-wax casting, and jewelry-making.

To produce a metal replica of the wax model, gold or some other metal is poured or forced into the sprue hole to fill the cavity left by the wax. When the metal has solidified, the mold is broken to remove the replica. After cleaning and polishing, one has a perfect metal copy of the wax model.

When discussing each step in the casting process, it is sometimes useful to compare and contrast the jewelry-making approach with other crafts that utilize lost-wax casting.

The six steps:

1. Make the model
2. Add wax sprues
3. Invest the model
4. Burn out the wax
5. Cast the object
6. Divest and finish the object

1. Make the model

Today most jewelry models are made from waxes used for jewelry making. The waxes are by-products of the petroleum industry; however, ancient metalworkers are more likely to have used beeswax or waxes and resins from plants or trees. Probably they combined different types of waxes to get desired physical characteristics, just as we do today.

The wax for sculpture or making jewelry can be used in several different ways. The model can be built up; it can be carved; it can be formed from sheet wax; or a combination of techniques may be used. A carving wax must be relatively hard because the technique may involve cutting with knives, saws, files, etc. If the wax is too soft, the saws and files simply clog up. On the other hand, a build-up process requires that layers of wax adhere to each other. A wax with a soft putty-like consistency when slightly warmed may be use for hand-formed sculpture. Buildup with a hot tool could be performed with a firmer wax. Sheet wax, which becomes flexible but not sticky when warmed, can be hand worked to make free-form objects.

Making models for lost-wax casting is a distinct art in itself, and we will not go into that here. Instead, we will assume that a wax model is already available. A wax model is a precise wax design that contains all the detail that is desired in the final product. Undesirable details, such as a scratch, will also be faithfully reproduced, because lost-wax casting produces an extremely precise reproduction of the model. Wax models of jewelry or jewelry findings may be purchased for a few dollars from a number of companies that sell tools and supplies to jewelers and craftsmen.

2. Add wax sprues

The first step in actually making a casting mold involves enclosing the wax model in a plaster-like substance that becomes the mold when the wax is melted and burned out. To make it possible for metal to enter the mold, passageways must be formed that lead from the model to the outside of the mold. These passageways are called sprues, although some sculptors and commercial foundry workers will call them *gates* and *vents*. A gate is a hole through which metal enters the mold, while a vent is a passageway that allows air or gases to escape when metal is poured into the mold. Both gates and vents must extend from the model to the outside of the finished mold.

Most jewelry molds do not contain vents. They are not generally needed, because the gases inside the mold escape through the porous material from which the mold is made. Rods to form sprues and vents are sometimes made from a wax that melts at a temperature lower than the wax model so the sprues and vents will melt first and allow the wax from the model to run out of the mold.

The sprues through which metal enters a mold are usually terminated at the outside of the mold in a pouring cup. This v-shaped segment of the sprue system guides metal into the sprue during the actual casting operation. The pouring cup may be formed from wax or simply scooped out of the soft investment from which the mold is made. Figure 2.1 shows a wax ring model that has been attached to a

**Figure 2.1
A wax model attached
to a rubber sprue base**

rubber sprue base. Visualize that when the invested mold is turned over the sprue extends to the surface of the mold. The dome in the sprue base forms a pouring cup in the hardened investment.

3. Invest the model

A mold for lost-wax casting is made by enclosing the model and sprue system with a material that will harden and withstand the elevated temperatures that are used for the rest of the process. Clay was undoubtedly the first substance used for making molds during the Bronze Age. The skills needed to make molds evolved from the pottery-making skills that were developed prior to the Bronze Age.

In an early text Theophilus describes the making of molds for lost-wax casting as covering the wax model with a layer of "sifted and well-mixed clay." Additional layers enclose this layer until a thick self-supporting mold is built up over the model. While not included in the passage about mold making, Theophilus elsewhere describes mixing clay with 25 percent horse dung; however, the reason for the addition is not explained. We now know that horse or cow dung is largely organic material that will improve the strength of the unfired mold, increase the porosity of the burned-out mold, and may affect the shrinkage of the mold. Later, in 1568, the famous sculptor and goldsmith, Benvenuto Cellini, described a method of mixing mold clay with "cloth frayings," apparently for similar reasons.

While clay was undoubtedly the investment material for ancient mold making, Cellini also describes the use of *gesso* for making small molds. Gesso is what we currently call *plaster of Paris*, an investment made from gypsum. Plaster of Paris mixed with ground-up old molds is currently used by many sculptors for making molds. Even more modern methods known as *ceramic-shell casting* are now being used by commercial founders. A ceramic-shell mold is simply a thin coating over the model that may be quickly fired to form a thin but strong mold. The firing time is very short because the mold is very thin.

Investment made primarily from gypsum is used for most gold and silver jewelry casting. Various forms of quartz and other additives are included to improve high-temperature characteristics and control shrinkage. Dental casting investment is virtually the same as investment produced for jewelry casting.

Platinum melts at higher temperatures than gold, silver, and brass and would severely degrade molds made from gypsum. Therefore, investment for platinum casting is made from compounds that result in a pure silicon-dioxide mold that will withstand much higher temperatures. All of the materials used for mold making are known as investment; consequently, the term *investment casting* is sometimes used to describe the lost-wax process. The procedures for preparing investment will be discussed in more detail in Chapter 6.

A mold made from clay, plaster, or a ceramic shell is not particularly strong. Consequently, some form of reinforcement is required to withstand the forces that occur when metal is injected into a mold. To prevent molds from breaking, ancient metalworkers cast bronze statues in casting pits with sand or earth packed around the mold to prevent fracture during the casting process. The procedure is still used today by founders using plaster or ceramic-shell molds.

In addition to packing the mold in sand while pouring bronze, the mold may be reinforced by wrapping with wire, a coarse wire screen, or sheet metal. While clay may be hand packed around a wax model, plaster of Paris investment is usually poured as a viscous liquid. Until the plaster investment hardens some sort of container is required to contain the fluid. This is called a *flask*. For jewelry and dental casting the flask is usually a segment of stainless steel pipe of sufficient size to hold the cast object. Jewelers use the term flask while dental technicians use the term *ring* for the same container such as shown in Figure 2.2.

Figure 2.2
A flask for jewelry or dental casting is a section of stainless steel pipe.

A flask made from a section of pipe provides both reinforcement and the container required for pouring a plaster mold. To seal the flask to contain the liquid investment, the bottom is often closed with a rubber device called a *sprue base*. A dome of rubber extends into the flask to form a pouring cup and provides a location for attaching the sprue extending from the model to the sprue base; hence, the name.

While archaeological evidence indicates that the techniques used for casting bronze statues were very similar to modern methods, we have found little evidence of the mold-making techniques used for making small objects. Because plaster made from gypsum has been around for millenia, it is entirely possible that some ancient founders may have used it for mold making in addition to clay.

4. Burn out the wax

Molds made from either clay or plaster must be burned out prior to casting. After the rubber sprue base is removed, the mold is placed in an oven with the sprue and pouring cup facing downwards. The *burnout* step accomplishes several things. First, the sprue wax melts, thus opening the sprue passageways so that the wax model can melt and drain from the mold cavity. Following conventional burnout instructions, after most of the wax has drained from the mold, the oven temperature is raised to a red heat to further harden and strengthen the mold. Finally, any wax that may have soaked into the investment is vaporized to render the investment somewhat porous.

For gypsum investment the furnace must be capable of reaching a temperature of 1400 degrees Fahrenheit or about 800 degrees Celsius. Both gypsum and clay go through changes when raised to high temperatures that convert the mold into a stronger, ceramic-like material. After burnout the molds are removed from the burnout oven for casting.

Sculptors place the mold in a casting pit and sand is packed around it for reinforcement when the metal is poured. Jewelry and dental flasks are simply removed from the oven and are ready to cast when the mold is at a suitable casting temperature. Jewelry is generally cast at elevated temperatures while sculpture molds are cooled to permit handling. Very large sculptures may be placed in a casting pit and burned out in place with the pouring cup facing upwards. A special drain, which is later plugged, must be provided to permit the wax to drain out. Burnout is accomplished by simply building the oven around the mold and later disassembling the oven before packing the mold in sand prior to casting.

5. Cast

Note that casting is described above as "injecting metal into the mold." With some types of casting, as is done commercially when making bronze statues or large machine parts, the metal is just poured into a large gate, and gravity causes the metal to flow throughout the mold while trapped air or gases escape through vents. This can be quite an event when a 13-ton statue is cast with a single pouring. However, in casting small objects such as jewelry, vents are not used and the molten metal will tend to solidify before the mold is filled unless extra force is used to drive the metal into the mold.

Investment casting requires an external force on the molten metal to drive air and gases out through the porous investment and fill the cavity before the metal freezes. *Centrifugal casting* is a casting technique that drives the metal into the mold by centrifugal force when the mold is spun rapidly.

Another technique is *vacuum-assisted casting*, in which a vacuum pump is used to draw gases from the bottom of the flask, creating a vacuum within the mold cavity that allows atmospheric pressure to force the molten metal into the mold. An example of entry-level equipment used for vacuum-assisted casting is shown in Figure 2.3.

Figure 2.3
Example of equipment for vacuum-assisted casting (Photo courtesy of KerrLab.)

A third method of forcing metal into the mold is called steam casting, in which steam is formed above the molten metal that, in turn, forces the metal into the mold. Sometimes compressed air pressure is used as well. These alternatives will be discussed later.

6. Divestment and cleanup

The obvious final step in lost-wax casting is to remove the investment and sprues from the cast object. This step varies somewhat depending on the size of the object and the metal that was cast. Small jewelry flasks are allowed to cool until the metal in the sprue turns from red to gray. Then the entire flask and mold is plunged into a bucket of water. The remaining heat generates a lot of steam and bubbles, and the mold simply disintegrates.

This method works well with gold castings; however, sterling silver may develop small fractures and appear brittle if it is quenched while the temperature is still too high. As a general rule, do not place the flask in water until the sprue opening no longer glows red.

Larger castings such as bronze statues are generally allowed to cool to room temperature, and the investment is removed by mechanical means, perhaps simply a hammer and chisel. If a jewelry flask is allowed to cool too much so that steam is not generated to break up the investment, mechanical methods and possibly a hammer and chisel will be required to remove the investment. The hammer and chisel approach is necessary when some of the harder gem stones are "cast in place" since plunging a hot flask into water would fracture the gemstones. More about this later.

Finally, sprues are cut off and the cast object is finished, using chisels, files, scrapers, sandpaper, and appropriate polishing methods. These differ little from the methods in ancient Greece as shown on ancient illustrated pottery in a Berlin museum. Modern sculptors and jewelers have pneumatically and electrically driven grinders and polishing equipment to speed matters up, but the approach is essentially the same. Some jewelry is finished using *mass-finishing techniques*, with vibrating or rotary tumblers that minimize hand labor.

3

Setting Up Shop

This chapter will *not* tell you everything you need to know to set up a casting shop. It *will* list some of the options and suggest the rationale for making some of the choices.

It is likely that the ancient sculptor or jeweler had to make his own tools and find most of his raw materials. Today, however, a number of companies exist that can provide all of the required equipment, tools, and supplies for lost-wax casting. Jewelers and dental technicians use essentially the same tools and supplies, so it is not surprising to discover that some of the jeweler's suppliers started out supporting dentists or dental laboratories.

If one wants to set up a shop to do lost-wax casting, several decisions must be made. Obviously, a person-sized sculpture could not be cast or burned out using flasks or burnout ovens suitable for casting dental crowns. Similarly, flasks suitable for casting a single dental crown would be much smaller than a flask suitable for casting a few dozen rings. The whole process of setting up a shop starts with a decision regarding the size of the castings to be made.

Some options

A look at the flasks that are commercially available will provide some indication of the casting options available. Figure 3.1 shows an assortment of various size flasks. The smallest size might be suitable for casting dental crowns or small jewelry pieces such as a single ring. On the other hand, even a dental technician might cast several crowns at one time, so a slightly larger flask might be chosen. I do a lot of my personal work with a dental casting machine that fits a flask that is 2 inches in diameter by 2-1/2 inches high. This is a convenient size for rings and small pendants or brooches.

To minimize labor cost, a commercial caster would choose a much larger flask to permit casting of perhaps 100 rings at a time. Sometimes perforated

Figure 3.1
An assortment of flasks available for investment casting (Photo courtesy of KerrLab)

flasks are chosen to minimize the resistance to the air escaping from the mold during the casting process. Figure 3.2 shows several large perforated flasks that require special vacuum casting machines.

Figure 3.2
Several large perforated flasks for vacuum-assisted casting (Photo courtesy of KerrLab)

Type of casting machine

Another decision that must be made before equipment is ordered is whether casting will be done using a centrifugal casting machine or a vacuum-assisted system. In small sizes the same flask can be used for either casting method; however, large casting trees or large models lead to another decision: whether to use solid or perforated flasks. At this point one has to make some additional major decisions regarding casting machines.

A small to medium-sized flask can be cast with either a low-priced centrifugal casting machine or a modestly priced vacuum system. A typical "broken-

Figure 3.3
A typical broken-arm
centrifugal casting
machine for small
flasks (Photo
courtesy of KerrLab)

arm" dental centrifugal casting machine suitable for
flasks up to about 2 inches in diameter is shown in
Figure 3.3. A variety of "straight arm" machines are
also available and one might debate the advantages
of each. The unique Neycraft centrifugal casting
machine shown in Figure 3.4 has the protective
safety shield attached to the rotating arm.

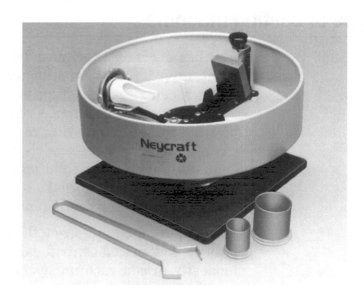

Figure 3.4
A Neycraft casting
machine with
protective shield
(Photo courtesy of
Neycraft)

Most of the horizontal spring-drive centrifugal casting machines are used for casting gold or silver, although some casters maintain that they can be used to cast platinum if the spring is wound up tighter to produce higher acceleration rates. Platinum is usually cast, however, using a vertical casting machine such as shown in Figure 3.5.

Figure 3.5

A vertical machine for platinum casting (Photo courtesy of The Contenti Company)

Vacuum-assisted casting is an alternative to centrifugal casting. The same solid wall flasks used with a centrifugal casting machine can be used with the entry-level vacuum-assisted casting machines shown in the last chapter. There are additional options available at increased cost.

Later, in Chapter 8, we will see that it becomes more difficult to develop an adequate casting vacuum in larger flasks. Therefore, to cast using large flasks suitable for hundreds of rings, some method must be used to decrease the resistance to removing air and gases from the mold. Of course, a more complicated vacuum-assisted casting machine with a well for the perforated flask is much more expensive. A casting machine suitable for perforated flasks is shown in Figure 3.6.

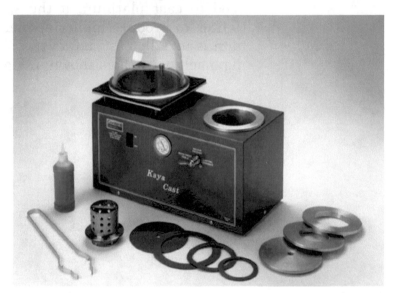

Figure 3.6
A vacuum-assisted casting machine for perforated flasks (Photo courtesy of The Contenti Company)

The above discussion ignores the controversy regarding the choice of vacuum-assisted or centrifugal casting. There are advocates of each approach and the relative merits of the choices are discussed in more detail in later chapters. All of the tools and equipment used for vacuum-assisted casting probably can be acquired for a lower total cost because the same machine is used both for removing bubbles from the investment and for casting. Centrifugal casting requires two machines: the centrifuge and the vacuum system for debubblizing.

Once the general approach to casting has been selected, there are many options available that range in price from a few hundred dollars to many thousands of dollars. Some commercial systems combine the vacuum-assisted system and the system for melting the casting metal.

Figure 3.7
A small electric
burnout oven suitable
for several small
flasks (Photo
courtesy of KerrLab)

Burnout ovens

Burnout ovens are the second major cost item in
any lost-wax casting shop. Once again the cost is
proportional to the size and/or the number of flasks
to be burned out at one time. Figure 3.7 shows a
small electric burnout oven suitable for processing
several small flasks or one somewhat larger flask.
The interior is a 6 by 6 by 6-inch cube. At the other
extreme is a large-capacity natural gas oven for volume production.

Most commercially available burnout ovens include
a temperature indicator to monitor the internal
temperature of the oven. *Thermocouple* temperature indicators are often called *pyrometers*. Some
burnout ovens include a microprocessor controller
to cause the oven to change temperature to corre-

spond to a particular burnout sequence. The rationale for choosing a specific burnout temperature profile will be discussed in a later chapter.

Choice of supplier

Once the main parameters are chosen, you merely have to select accessories and tools that match the flask sizes selected. A large flask requires an appropriately sized container for mixing investment, scales with the correct weight range, etc. Probably one would benefit from attending a casting workshop to experience the entire lost-wax casting process before making any choices.

There are a large number of tool and equipment suppliers throughout the world. An extensive list is provided in the Appendix. These suppliers vary all the way from small one- or two-man operations to large organizations with a world-wide clientele. The price that one may pay for a specific item may very considerably too.

If you are computer literate, many of the companies have a web presence and it is very easy to order supplies and equipment over the Internet. Everything shows up reliably at your office or doorstep a few days later.

Several companies manufacture investment. It is likely that you will choose the investment offered to you by your first instructor. However, there are a few options. First, gold and silver, or any metal that melts below 2000° F is cast in a gypsum-based investment. Platinum requires a special investment due to the higher melting temperature, and it will not be considered here.

The two major investment manufacturers in the United States, Kerr®, founded in 1891, and Ransom

& Randolph, founded in 1872, both have a premium product: Satin Cast™ from Kerr®, and Ultra Vest™ from R&R®. Most jewelry supply companies offer one or both of the premium products in addition to a number of less expensive formulas. Large tool and equipment suppliers may offer their own brand of investment such as Westcast™ from Rio Grande®.

Gypsum investment contains less than 30 percent gypsum (also known as plaster of Paris) plus additional fillers that generally include some form of quartz or silicon dioxide. Sometimes there are other agents to minimize oxidation. The exact formula is, of course, proprietary. The final choice will again likely depend on your first instructor and personal experiments that may follow.

Gold and silver casting alloys may be purchased from many of the tool and equipment suppliers. However, a number of metal-processing companies may be found that can supply a variety of casting alloys in addition to processing precious metal scrap. Again the Internet is a source of much information including extensive hints on casting and alloy selection.

The following search phrases will produce a lot of valuable information when typed into one of several "search engines" such as Google or Yahoo. Many of the "hits" will be in the hobby or crafts category, but you will also find the major suppliers as well.

Search phrases (enclose in quotes):
- "jewelry supplies"
- "jewelers tools"
- "lost wax casting"
- "refining precious metals"
- "cire perdue".

4

The Model

Overview

The starting point for lost-wax casting is a model, usually made of wax. Other materials may be used for the model, but the technique is still called lost-wax casting. The Greeks used beeswax to create models for lost-wax casting 2500 years ago. Today, sculptors and jewelers use man-made waxes derived from petroleum, perhaps combined with animal or vegetable waxes to obtain special physical characteristics. The end result is the same: a model that will disappear to produce a mold cavity that can be filled with metal.

Wax models are created by carving, fabrication, or build up.

Wax models are created using several distinctly different techniques.

1. The model can be carved, starting with a block of hard wax.

2. It can be built up from drops of molten wax.

3. It can be fabricated from sheet wax, wax wire, and drops of molten wax.

4. Duplicate models can be made by injecting molten wax into a mold previously made of rubber from a metal model.

The process of making original wax models is a specialty in itself and is thoroughly covered in a number of textbooks. This chapter contains a discussion of the waxes and other substances that may be used for model making.

About waxes

Waxes are obtained either from animals, insects, plants, or minerals, or are chemically synthesized. One wax from an insect source is beeswax, collected from the honeycombs of bees. This is a rather brittle wax that softens at body temperature. Usually, rosin or other vegetable resins are added to beeswax to obtain more desirable characteristics. Carnauba wax, from a Brazilian wax palm, has been used to harden beeswax.

Modern wax models are almost universally made from waxes derived as a by-product from petroleum processing. Two general classes of waxes are made from petroleum. One is a brittle variety of wax called paraffin, such as is used to seal glass jars in home canning. The other is microcrystalline wax. Some authors refer to a third wax type called *petrolatum* that is commonly used in the manufacture of ointments and cosmetics. It is a mixture of microcrystalline wax and about 10 percent mineral oil.

The microcrystalline waxes are obtained when more volatile paraffins and oils are distilled from petroleum, leaving the solid waxes behind. Generally, they are not brittle, and different fractions produce waxes with various degrees of hardness, ductility, and melting points, depending upon the amount of oils remaining in the product. Physically, one of the microcrystalline waxes is soft and works much like beeswax. Other microcrystalline waxes are very hard and may be machined almost like metal. All microcrystalline waxes can be softened by mixing with mineral oil or petroleum jelly.

Model-making wax is a by-product of the petroleum industry

Model-making waxes are made from microcrystalline waxes that are produced as a by-product by petroleum companies. For example, at one time the Mobil Oil Company sold a wax known as Modeling Wax, Formula 2300. A search of the Internet does not locate this particular formula; however, the search term "microcrystalline wax" turns up a variety of products for sculptors and jewelers.

Artists and craftsmen are more likely to obtain their wax supplies from distributors that formulate waxes with specific properties from natural and synthetic sources with various melting points. Some distributors offer a variety of shapes that are more directly applicable to the needs of jewelers, dentists, and sculptors. Companies such as Kerr®, and Ferris® manufacture sheet wax, block wax, wire wax, and waxes in other special shapes. Injection waxes for reproducing multiple wax models are available in cakes or beads. Wax ring tubes are made of hard waxes that may be sawed, filed, and carved to form models for rings. Special wax rods and wires called sprue wax are made from lower melting point waxes so that they will melt first during burnout to open the channel and allow melting and vaporizing model wax to escape. Sticky wax is used to weld wax parts together.

Microcrystalline and paraffin waxes soften and melt at temperatures that range from below 100° F (38° C) to about 300° F (149° C). Petroleum companies and wax distributors may formulate, or mix, two or more petroleum, animal, or vegetable waxes with other materials to obtain the characteristics needed for each application. Inert colors are generally added to different waxes for identification purposes; however, there is no color-coding standard and similar colors used by different manufacturers may indicate different properties. In other words, color alone will not help you identify the properties of a particular wax unless you know the color scheme of the particular manufacturer.

Waxes are sometimes combined with plastics, such as polyethylene, to produce flexible models that are more durable and easier to remove from rubber molds than models made from basic microcrystalline waxes. These have names such as Plast-O-Wax®, which suggests the combination of wax and plastic. The exact formulation is generally patented or a trade secret.

Lost-plant and Lost-bug casting

Earlier it was suggested that models could be made of materials other than wax. Actually, any organic object can be used as a model for lost-wax casting. Bugs, for example, make fine models, and one may call this "lost-bug" casting. Plants and flowers have been successfully reproduced by "lost-plant" casting. Practically any plastic object can be used as a model, although some plastics may produce unpleasant or even noxious fumes during burnout. The only requirement is that the object must burn out cleanly and leave no residue that cannot be vaporized by heating the flask to about 1300° F (704° C). Some sea creatures such as starfish may leave a gritty residue that will affect the surface texture of the casting. Experiments with a cockroach model resulted in non-vaporized residue after burnout. Sometimes it is possible to dump the residue out the sprue hole, but casting any non-wax model is an experiment.

Sculptors sometimes use polystyrene foam for making models. These may be sand cast by simply pouring hot metal into the mold without any previous burnout, and the polystyrene simply vaporizes and diffuses into the sand. It is unclear whether this would work for investment casting without burnout. The polystyrene model could be removed from an investment mold by dissolving it with acetone. If the surface texture of the polystyrene foam is undesirable, wax can be used to cover the foam texture and produce a smooth object or an object with additional artistic work on the wax. One might wish to dissolve the foam with acetone and then burn out the wax. These suggestions are just now being explored and are experimental methods that might be used to broaden the conventional lost-wax technique.

It is not necessary for a jeweler to make wax models; wax patterns are available from many sources and represent objects from complete jewelry items like rings, for example, to wax jewelry parts or findings, which may be assembled to produce a complete model. For most of the discussions in the following chapters, we will assume that a wax model is available. However, in the next chapter some consideration will be given to the way different model shapes and masses may affect how sprues are attached.

Wax welding

The tools required for wax welding are not numerous or expensive. A small number of repairs could be made using a wax-welding tool made by sticking a large needle into the eraser of a pencil. More

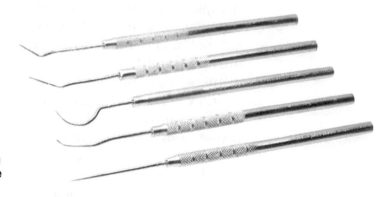

robust tools, shown in Figure 4.1, may be purchased
from a jewelry supply company or can be homemade
by obtaining old worn-out dental tools that can be
heated with a torch and reshaped as shown. Either
tool may be heated using an alcohol lamp or even a
candle. Electrically heated wax-welding tools such
as shown in Figure 4.2 are also available.

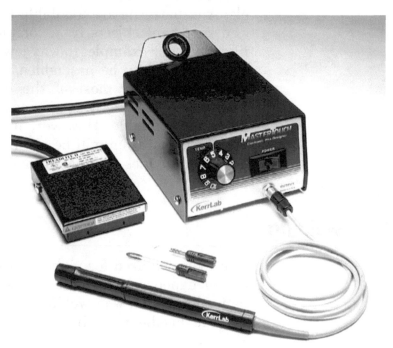

The basic wax-manipulation techniques that are valuable to the caster are the same as those used by wax designers. The skill of welding two pieces of wax together is fundamental. In some cases it is possible to simply hold two pieces of wax close together while heating both sides of the joint with a wax-welding tool. Then quickly press the two objects together and hold immobile until the wax has solidified and has sufficient strength to support the joint. This is essentially all one needs to know to crudely attach sprues to wax models as shown in Figure 4.3.

**Figure 4.3
Welding a sprue to a wax model**

Once the wax has hardened, smooth the joint with a heated tool. One problem with the above welding technique is that the two sides of the joint are melted slightly and the completed weld may be compressed so that the final dimensions of the object are less than before the weld. Pressing the two pieces together probably will squeeze a bead of wax out of the joint allowing the two pieces to move closer together. When dimensions must be held precisely, a different welding technique must be used.

In precision wax welding, it is important to add a little wax to the joint rather than squeezing wax out. Do this by heating the welding tool and quickly dipping it into some welding wax before touching the joint. When the heated tool is withdrawn from the welding wax, a blob of molten wax will be attached to the tip of the tool. Transfer this quickly to the site of the joint where the heated tool will slightly melt the two wax pieces to be joined and the blob of wax will add material to reinforce the joint.

It is not wise to attempt to weld two pieces of wax together by simply heating the joint with the welding tool alone. While the joint may stick together, the hot tool will "pick up" a small blob of wax, leaving a slight recess rather than a nicely welded joint.

A slightly different approach, with the same objective, is to hold a small piece of fine wax wire near the object to be welded. Instead of pressing the heated welding tool into a pot of designer's wax, the heated tool is touched to the wax wire near the end to pick up a small glob of wax. A reproducible amount of wax can be picked up each time by "cutting off" a specific very short length of wax wire. The length of wax wire determines the size of the little mound of wax at the joint. It will probably not be possible to get a perfectly flat surface at the welded joint. Instead, a little ridge will extend along the welded joint. This is, in fact, desirable. When the joint has hardened, the ridge may be filed, sanded, or carved down to produce a clean, smooth joint.

In some ways working wax is just like working metal. File down the ridge of wax and sand smooth until the joint cannot be seen. If the welding wax is a different color from the objects being welded, smooth the joint until the ridge along the joint cannot be felt with the finger. Sand with progressively finer grades of sandpaper, burnish the surface with a piece of a business card, and then finish the surface by buffing it with a scrap piece of nylon stocking material. This final buffing works just like buffing metal and produces a highly polished surface. Undesirable grooves or scratches may be filled the same way. Simply place a row of dots of wax along the scratch with the heated tool that has been dipped into a block or container of wax. Add dots of wax until there is a ridge along the entire scratch, and then file, sand, and buff to produce a scratch-free surface.

Repair of models

While the design of wax models for casting is an art in itself, the ability to repair and modify waxes should be one of the skills of a caster. Wax models obtained from a commercial source are fragile and may arrive with cracks or otherwise damaged. Because lost-wax casting is such a precision process, even scratches in the wax model will result in an imperfect casting. Although it may be possible to obtain a replacement, it is often more expedient to repair the model than complain.

Ring resizing is easier in wax

In other circumstances it may be desirable to modify a model. For example, resizing a wax ring model is simpler than completing the casting and then resizing the finished metal ring. To reduce the size of a ring, a section of wax is removed from the shank and the joint is closed and welded. If the ring is to be enlarged, a piece of wax is added to the cut shank. The added segment must be the correct length, but otherwise the wax may be larger in cross section than the shank being repaired. When the joints have hardened, the extra segment of wax is carved to match the rest of the shank. File, sand, and polish until the added segment cannot be detected by touch.

To complete a joint, a number of blobs of wax are added as described above all around or along the desired joint. Some workers prefer to use a designer's wax of a different color from the object being repaired so that the completeness of the joint may be observed easily. Let's look at these steps in more detail to repair a broken shank on a wax model for a ring.

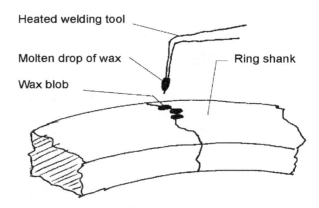

Figure 4.4
Tacking a ring shank together to hold a precise ring size

It is necessary to hold the two adjoining pieces together and then weld the joint in such a way as not to change the final ring size. To do this, simply hold the two sides of the joint together and insert a heated tool into the crack to create a small melted dot right at the joint. A little wax is melted on each side of the crack. This is shown in Figures 4.4. When the wax hardens the two pieces will be welded together only at that point, which is usually insufficient to hold the two pieces together.

To get a good joint, the process is repeated all along the crack, which then becomes a continuous welded joint. This creates a surface weld, because the melted region may not penetrate the whole thickness of the joint. Go around the whole joint on all sides to get a substantial weld as shown in Figure 4.5.

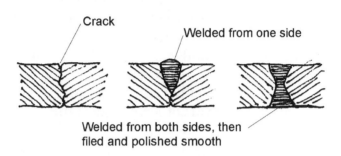

Crack

Welded from one side

Welded from both sides, then
filed and polished smooth

**Figure 4.5
Completing a "tack"
weld to hold a ring
shank together**

The key to making a satisfactory wax weld is the step where the heated tool is pressed into some scrap wax or a pot of designer's wax before attempting to weld the joint. As noted before, this adds a little wax to the weld rather than removing wax from the model and leaving a depression.

When resizing wax ring models, one must be careful to not reduce or increase the size to a point that the shape of the rest of the ring is damaged. Some designs cannot be changed more than a couple of ring sizes without distorting the head of the ring.

Modifying a wax model

In addition to modifying the size of a wax ring model, the whole design can be altered using the same welding techniques just described. Often custom designs are made by merely modifying a commercial wax rather than by developing a completely new design. The modification may vary all the way from a simple addition of accessory stones to a merging of large elements from two or more commercial waxes. Wax shanks without attached heads for stones may be obtained, and wax heads of the proper size may be added to use a customer's stones.

Figure 4.6 shows sample wax shanks to which heads may be added. Alternatively, one could cut the head from one wax model and attach it to a different ring. Wax models of pins or pendants may be cut apart and re-created as rings using wax shanks molded separately or cut from other wax models. Once the step has been taken to modify or revise commercial wax models, one is on the way to the craft of jewelry design.

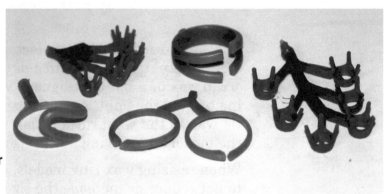

**Figure 4.6
Selection of wax
shanks and heads
suitable for original or
modified designs**

Sheet wax and wax wire of various shapes can be used to produce original designs using basic welding techniques that are little different from those used for repair and modification. Completely original models are made either by carving the shape from a block of wax or by building up a design by adding pieces of various wax shapes or blobs of wax. But that is another story.

Finishing wax models

The lost-wax process is a precision casting method and the final reproduction will show every detail of the wax model. Wax models can be very crudely made and final finishing left until the casting is complete. This procedure results in a lot of work. A much better approach is to produce a fine finish and polish on the wax model, which will then become evident in the cast reproduction. If the wax model is polished, the casting will have a relatively good polish.

Commercial casters strive to have the casting come out practically finished so that only the sprue must be cut off and dressed before the piece is placed in a vibrating tumbler for final finishing. If repairs or joints are made with a relatively hard Designer's Wax, the repaired piece can be finished with a file and sandpaper just as if it were a metal object. Simply file off any excess lumps of wax and sand the surface down to match the surrounding area. It is useful to use a fine, single-cut file followed by 300- and 600-grit sandpaper. A *file card*, which looks like a brush with metal bristles, is used to clean the wax out of the file. A final high polish is obtained by rubbing the surface with an old piece of nylon stocking material.

There are also wax-polishing fluids that will slightly melt the wax surface to produce a polished finish. Some artists are adept at quickly passing the piece through the flame of an alcohol lamp to obtain a smooth polished finish. All of the above methods require some trial-and-error experience. The file, sandpaper, and nylon stocking material finishing sequence is recommended because it closely matches similar metal-working techniques.

A ring design for students

While the purpose of this book is not to teach wax design in great detail, a simple design for an opal ring is included to show the steps required for designing a ring to fit a free-form opal cabochon. To keep the description short, we will assume some experience in jewelry making and will not define a number of new terms. The finished ring, shown in Figure 4.7, is based on an approach developed by Dr. Paul Downing that provides much better support and security for opals than the commercial findings that are generally available.

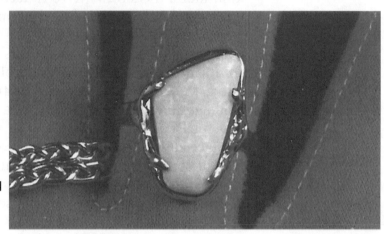

Figure 4.7
Simple ring design recommended by Paul Downing to support and protect an Opal

The ring is started with a piece of wax bezel wire. Partially finished 6- or 8-gauge wax bezel wire is suggested. Uncut wax bezel wire is also available, but this is more massive with square corners that require more finishing work.

First, place a layer of Scotch or masking tape around the edge of the stone. This makes the stone slightly larger when the bezel is fitted directly on the stone and makes it easier to insert the stone into the final casting. Wrap the wax bezel wire around the stone and cut to the proper length. Using the methods described above, weld the ends of the wax bezel wire together just as if you were making a bezel of metal.

When the bezel is welded together, add four or more prongs made from 12- or 14-gauge half-round wax wire. Set these prongs right on top of the bezel wire rather than along the side. The prongs will be used to hold the stone in place instead of attempting to roll the bezel of the finished ring.

Next, add a ring shank of 8-gauge half-round wax wire. The ring shank, which can be a complete circle or a partial circle, can then be welded to the bezel. Gently press the stone out of the bezel and reinforce the bezel joint on the inside where it was obscured by the stone. Cut away any excess so that the stone will still seat in the wax model. Additional wax can be added to dress up joints and create a finished wax model.

After casting, clean up the ring and open up the seat with a flex shaft tool and burs, if necessary. Dress the half-round prongs to an appropriate length so that they may be bent over slightly to hold the stone in place. This is much safer than trying to turn a bezel.

The stone is finally set in place by making a small bead of epoxy around the seat of the bezel and inserting the stone. This seat will provide support for the stone around its entire perimeter rather than at a few locations as in a typical prong setting. When the prongs are turned over the stone, a very small dot of epoxy under each prong will provide a cushion and prevent stone damage should the ring be struck against anything. The seat epoxy and the dot of epoxy beneath each prong should be invisible to the naked eye. The security and protection provided by this setting is remarkable and has saved opals that otherwise could have been severely damaged.

This ring setting, or a pendant using similar techniques, is recommended for a design project that may be used by experienced students instead of buying commercial waxes for a workshop.

References

Hiroshi Tsuyuki, *Basic Wax Modeling*, Matsubara-Kashiwa Books, Tokyo, 1990.

Hiroshi Tsuyuki and Yoko Ohba, *Practical Wax Modeling*, ASQ Corp., Southfield, MI, 1994.

Roger Armstrong, *Wax and Casting*, Star Publishing, Belmont, CA, 1989.

G. W. Skinner, *Proceedings of the National Bronze Casting Conference*, University of Kansas, 1960.

H. Bennett, *Industrial Waxes*, Vol. I and Vol. II, Chemical Publishing, New York, 1975.

Paul B. Downing, *Opal Cutting Made Easy*, Majestic Press, Tallahassee, FL, 1984.

5

Placing Sprues

Overview

Sprues are passageways through which metal enters a mold. A *founder*, one who usually pours cast iron, brass, or bronze, may use the term *gates* to refer to the same openings. The precise term may not be important, but the precise location of each sprue is important for quality casting.

Jewelry investment becomes porous during burnout and thus does not need vents.

Whenever molten metal enters a mold, it must displace air or gases trapped in the mold cavity. If the mold is made of an impermeable material such as metal or clay, passageways must be created for the gases to escape. These openings are called *vents*. The term *riser* is sometimes used to denote another type of cavity purposely placed within a mold. Most jewelers and dental technicians use investment for making the mold, which becomes porous during burnout and thus does not need vents. However, to produce quality castings using investment molds, the caster must understand the reasoning behind the correct placement of gates, vents, sprues, and risers.

Figure 5.1 represents a mold cavity surrounded by

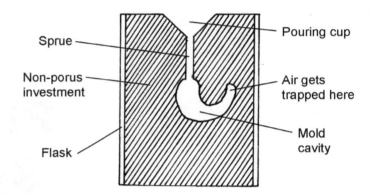

Figure 5.1
Cross-section of a mold surrounded by an impermeable block of investment

an impermeable block of investment. If one simply pours metal into the pouring cup, the metal will soon plug up the gate or sprue and trapped gases will prevent the metal from completely filling the mold. On the other hand, if a vent is added as shown in Figure 5.2, the gases within the mold are no longer trapped, and the mold can fill completely.

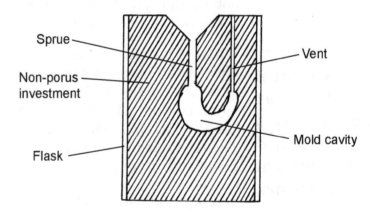

Figure 5.2
Cross-section of a flask with a vent added to permit gases to escape from mold cavity

Sculptors often use the "bottom feed" that includes a long sprue to the bottom of the mold, while several vents permit air and gases to escape from the top of the mold. The long descending sprue allows the weight of the column of metal to apply pressure that helps fill the mold completely.

Jewelers and dental technicians generally use different approaches from sculptors, because investments used for jewelry or dental work are designed to become porous during burnout. The pores are small and do not affect the surface finish of the casting; however, they are large enough to permit gases to be displaced from the cavity, especially if extra force is used to drive the metal into the mold cavity.

Metal must be forced into a mold to expel gases

Centrifugal casting or compressed air casting causes metal to be injected into the mold cavity with sufficient force to expel the trapped gases from the mold through the porous investment. Steam casting uses the pressure caused by the expansion of water into steam to force the metal into the mold, and thus force the gases out of the mold. Vacuum-assisted casting involves using a vacuum pump to remove the gas from the mold cavity so that ordinary atmospheric pressure can force metal into the mold. It is the same physical principle that allows us to suck on a straw and have atmospheric pressure force fluid up the straw. We often think that the vacuum pump is sucking the metal into the mold. However, it is more technically correct to realize that an atmospheric pressure of about 15 pounds per square inch is pressing on the metal in the pour cup, and this forces the liquid metal into the cavity after the vacuum pump removes the trapped gas and creates a vacuum.

Controlled shrinkage

There are other factors to consider in the placement of sprues besides the escape of gases from the mold. Most metals shrink as they cool. However, it is not desirable for the casting to end up smaller than the mold. If the cast object starts to shrink and no molten metal is available to continue filling the mold, shrinkage imperfections, called *porosities,* will form. The sprue must be designed and attached in such a way as to permit additional metal from the pouring cup or other reservoirs to enter the mold during the cooling process. This is why jewelers and dental technicians always must calculate the amount of metal to be sufficient to form a button in the bottom of the pour cup.

Controlling shrinkage is probably the single most important concept ... to produce quality castings.

Other methods are used to produce the same result. Founders may add risers that store additional molten metal to supply the shrinking metal in the mold cavity. Risers may be particularly important if an unusually shaped object does not permit sprues to be attached to all of the heavier masses of the object.

Controlling shrinkage is probably the single most important concept that must be understood in order to produce quality castings. Metal alloys for casting do not solidify at a specific temperature as do pure metals such as copper or 24-karat gold. Instead, metal alloys "freeze," or solidify, over a range of temperatures, and this progressive solidification affects the size a sprue should be and where sprues should be placed on a wax model. Because the concept of progressive freezing and the effect on sprue placement is sometimes difficult to understand, some further illustrations may help.

Assume that a ring to be cast consists of a massive head attached to a thin shank. Before investing, a wax sprue must be connected to the wax model to form a passageway for metal to enter the mold. If the sprue were attached to the shank of the ring, as shown in Figure 5.3, the metal would freeze in the

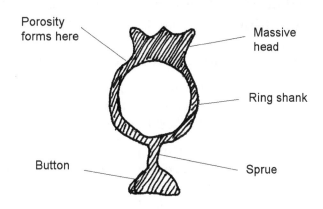

**Figure 5.3
Ring with massive
head showing
porosity that develops
from improper
sprueing**

sprue and narrow section of the mold before the larger mass solidifies. Frozen metal in the sprue and narrow part of the object would prevent metal from entering the more massive part of the mold cavity and shrinkage porosity probably would result near the location where the head is attached to the shank. This is because the shrinking mass tries to draw metal into the large mass from the area near the already solidified sprue. Because there is insufficient metal to fill the large mass, the resulting shrinkage leaves a lot of little pits in the shank and perhaps a larger cavity in the center of the large mass.

Sprues should always be attached to the more massive parts of the model. Sprues should always be large enough to freeze after the segment of the object to which the sprue is attached. More than one sprue may be necessary if there are multiple masses separated by thinner regions. This permits molten metal to be drawn from the button as the casting hardens progressively. Because the button is the last mass to freeze, shrinkage porosity is limited to the button or along the sprue attached to the button.

Rules for attaching sprues

As a general rule: *Sprues should be attached to the most massive elements of a model and each sprue should be of sufficient diameter to not freeze before the object freezes.*

As a second general rule: *Where there are multiple massive elements in the model, a sprue should be attached to each major mass.*

The third general rule is a result of the first rule: *The cross-sectional area of a sprue should be greater than the cross-sectional area of the mass to which it is attached.* Of course, this is to allow the metal in the sprue to remain molten to supply additional metal to shrinking metal in the cooling cast object.

Where the surface contours of the model are complex, be sure to attach the sprue to a convex surface because it is generally easier to cut off the sprue and finish up a surface that is convex than one that is concave.

Risers are sometimes attached to models when the shape of the object makes it inconvenient to have a sprue attached to each major mass. The riser is a reservoir to supply molten metal to the cooling object such as shown in Figure 5.4. While risers are more commonly seen in bronze statuary casting, the same approach could be used to prevent shrinkage porosity on some complex jewelry castings.

Figure 5.5 shows special sprues designed for steam casting which will be described in more detail later.

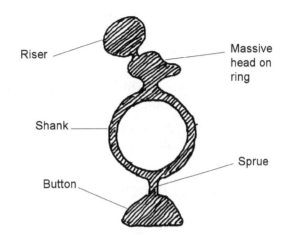

Riser

Massive head on ring

Shank

Sprue

Button

Figure 5.4
Illustration showing how a riser can be used to supply metal to a massive ring head to prevent shrinkage porosity

The small sprues enter a ball of wax and a larger sprue that is attached to the model. The total cross-sectional area of the three small sprues should equal the cross-sectional area of the large sprue, so that a sufficient metal flow can be achieved. Because the small sprues will freeze before the large sprue, a ball of wax is included as shown to form a metal mass that will supply molten metal to the cooling object when the casting is made. It functions as a riser. The sprue between the wax ball (riser) and the model should be large enough and only about 1/8 inch long.

Figure 5.5
Special sprues for steam casting with balls on the sprue that function as risers

Finally, as a precaution, sprues are often made with a wax with a lower melting point than the rest of the wax model. This allows the sprue to melt first during wax elimination or burnout and prevents any possible pressure buildup that could result if the model were to melt before the sprue. For convenience, many casters do not take this precaution and obtain perfectly satisfactory results.

Welding sprues to models

Sprues can be attached to a model simply by heating the sprue and pressing it against the model. Such a joint will not be very strong but additional heating could strengthen it. A better approach would be to add wax to the joint with a heated tool as described earlier.

Little wax fillets as shown in Figure 5.6 should be

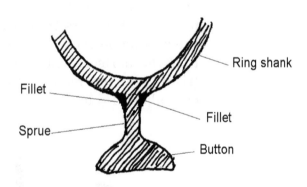

Figure 5.6
Wax fillets are added to the junctions between sprue and model to prevent turbulence in flowing metal during casting.

added to cause a smooth transition between the sprue and the object. A *fillet* is a rounding of an internal angle to avoid sharp corners that cause turbulence in the metal flowing into a model during casting. The turbulence may result in improper solidification and casting imperfections. Fillets should always be added to the junction between sprues and models and between sprue segments so that no sharp or abrupt junctions are present.

Sticky wax is a special wax with a low melting point that readily sticks to other waxes. It is available in rods or chunks, and in small tins. Sticky wax may be used to attach sprues to models. Because it is often convenient to use regular modeling wax for attaching sprues, a common use for sticky wax is to attach many models to the main trunk sprue when casting many models using a tree.

Take a heated tool, or heat a re-shaped dental probe in an alcohol flame. Hold the model and sprue near each other so that both pieces may be heated simultaneously with the tool. When both surfaces have melted, press together and hold in place until the wax solidifies. While the sprue may be firmly attached to the ring shank at this point, the spruing operation is not complete. More wax must be flowed

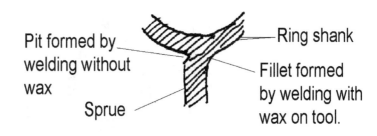

Figure 5.7
Results of welding sprue with and without wax on the welding tool

into the joint to form the fillet shown on the right side of Figure 5.7. If one simply tries to heat the junction between the sprue and model, the wax will stick to the tool and cause a cavity to form as shown on the left side. Instead, the heated probe should be pressed into sticky wax and removed to lift a drop of wax on the probe tip. Then while the drop is still fluid, touch the junction between the sprue and model, and the drop will form a neat fillet. Repeat all around the sprue so that there are no sharp corners.

Once all sprues have been attached to the model, the model and all attached sprues should be weighed carefully, and the weight should be recorded to permit later calculation of the amount of metal to be used for the casting. Of course, the sprues should be cut to approximately the final length or the wrong weight will be calculated.

Finally, using extra wax when necessary, attach the model and sprue to a sprue base as shown in Figure 5.8, and everything is ready for investing. Rubber sprue bases are available in a number of sizes to seal the end of a flask and provide a location to attach the sprue.

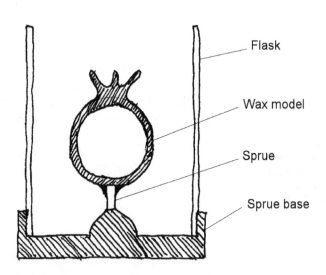

Flask

Wax model

Sprue

Sprue base

**Figure 5.8
Model and sprue
attached to sprue
base ready for
investing**

Venting to increase investment porosity

While this discussion will be emphasized in the chapter on vacuum-assisted casting, the subject is brought up here because vents are part of the spruing process. Incomplete castings sometimes result when using non-perforated flasks because the investment around a model is not sufficiently porous for the trapped gases to be expelled during casting. This can result when a large model or tree containing many models is enclosed in a large flask. Examine Figure 8.2 to see how molds near the upper end of a flask will not be sufficiently evacuated by the vacuum pump during vacuum-assisted casting.

To reduce the resistance to airflow, a wax grid can

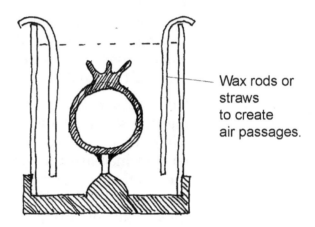

Wax rods or straws to create air passages.

Figure 5.9
A commercial wax grid or simple rods or straws are used to produce additional air passages to reduce resistance to air flow during casting

be inserted around the perimeter of the flask. This will be eliminated during burnout, producing additional passageways for gas to be evacuated from the upper molds. The wax grid has an effect similar to adding vents to a mold; however, the grid is not directly attached to the model. The same effect can be produced, as shown in Figure 5.9, by sticking pieces of sprue wax into the investment around the model while making sure that the extra pieces of sprue wax do not project completely through the investment. Perforated flasks, which will be described later in the vacuum-casting chapter, are also used to minimize the resistance to air or gas flow when using large flasks.

Other considerations

There is some debate regarding the shape of the sprue junction with the model. I have taught that the junction should be flared. That is, a fillet of wax should be added completely around the sprue-model junction as described earlier to permit a smooth flow of metal from the sprue into the model cavity. The fillet will eliminate any sharp corner or point of investment that could break off and damage the casting. The metal will also slow as it enters the model cavity and will be less likely to erode the walls of the mold.

On the other hand, others argue that instead of flaring, the sprue should be necked down at the point where it is attached to the model. This will act as a jet and increase the velocity of the metal entering the mold cavity and possibly will reduce the likelihood of metal freezing in the sprue. In my opinion, the benefits of flaring the junction outweigh the possible benefits of increasing the velocity of the flowing metal.

Investing

Overview

In the foundry context, the verb *to invest* means to envelop or surround, and that is just what one does when making a mold in the lost-wax process. Investment is the material used to make the mold. In ancient times clay was generally used to invest a wax model, which was later placed in a furnace to eliminate or burn out the wax prior to casting. Treatises on metalworking written in the twelfth century describe making investment of clay mixed with manure. Later Benvenuto Cellini described making molds using *gesso*, which is a term for what is now called plaster of Paris or simply gypsum plaster.

Most investments for casting gold and silver are formulated using gypsum as a binder. Investments made from gypsum start to degrade into sulfur compounds above 1350° F (732° C). They are usable with metals with melting points up to slightly above 2000° F (1093° C) because the very hot metal is only briefly in contact with the investment. Platinum casting requires special investment suitable for higher temperatures.

Investing a wax model is simple in concept: merely pour fluid investment into a flask to surround the model. After the investment hardens, melt out the wax. But there are other details to consider: Properly mixed investment has the consistency of thick cream. It tends to trap air while being mixed, forming little air bubbles in the investment. If the mold is poured with air still in the investment, the little bubbles become attached to the model. The final result is small spheres of metal attached to the final casting that must then be removed. Several approaches have been developed to prevent this from happening and thus produce quality castings.

Preparing the model

When water contacts a wax material, strong surface tension forces occur at the interface. For this reason liquid investment may not fill all the details of a model. Furthermore, trapped air bubbles may become attached to the surface of the wax model. Wetting agents are used to reduce both of these defects. Some wetting agents are painted or sprayed onto the model prior to investing to minimize bubbles or trapped air spaces. Vibrators are sometimes used to cause bubbles to rise to the top of the liquid investment and escape. Some investments are produced with a built-in wetting agent, and the model surface should not be covered with an additional wetting agent when using them. The model may be cleaned with alcohol, but it should be allowed to dry so that the alcohol will not dilute and weaken the investment near the model.

Mixing investment

Manufacturers' instructions generally specify that gypsum investment should be mixed with a ratio of

Table 6.1   Mixing Chart - To determine investment and water requirements for flasks of various sizes.

Flask Diameter	Height of Flask							
	2"	2-1/2"	3"	3-1/2"	4"	5"	6"	7"
2"	150 g 60 ml	175 g 70 ml	200 g 80 ml	250 g 100 ml	300 g 120 ml	350 g 140 ml		
2-1/2"	225 g 90 ml	300 g 120 ml	350 g 140 ml	400 g 160 ml	450 g 180 ml	575 g 230 ml		
3"	350 g 140 ml	425 g 170 ml	500 g 200 ml	600 g 240 ml	700 g 280 ml	850 g 340 ml	1025 g 410 ml	1250 g 500 ml
3-1/2"	450 g 180 ml	575 g 230 ml	675 g 270 ml	800 g 320 ml	900 g 360 ml	1150 g 460 ml	1375 g 550 ml	1600 g 640 ml
4"	500 g 200 ml	650 g 260 ml	750 g 300 ml	900 g 360 ml	1150 g 460 ml	1375 g 550 ml	1600 g 640 ml	1825 g 730 ml
5"					1700 g 680	2150 g 860 ml	2500 g 1000 ml	2975 g 1190 ml

40 parts water to 100 parts investment by weight. Less water produces a stronger mold but the mixture is very thick and it is difficult to eliminate any bubbles trapped in the mixture. Additional water thins the mixture but weakens the mold significantly, so the 40:100 ratio is about optimum for jewelry or dental investment. A weak mold may allow pieces of hardened investment to break off inside the cavity with resulting imperfections in the casting.

One milliliter of water weighs one gram

If dry investment is weighed in grams, water may be measured in milliliters or cubic centimeters fluid measure. A cubic centimeter of water at room temperature weighs approximately one gram. Tables may be calculated to permit measurement using other units such as ounces or pounds; however, the metric measures permit convenient calculations. Table 6.1 shows appropriate water and investment amounts for several flask sizes.

Most investment mixing instructions recommend that the investment should be added to water rather than the reverse. This will insure that the dry investment is completely saturated with water and that no clumps of dry powder remain. I have found it convenient to add water to a small amount of investment and then mix with a cooking whip. No doubt this approach introduces significant air to the mixture, but the approach has been successful when followed by a vacuuming step to eliminate the air bubbles. When larger quantities of investment are mixed, it should be added a little at a time to the water to insure that all investment is adequately saturated.

Removing trapped air

As mentioned before, if precautions are not taken bubbles inevitably become attached to the wax model during the investment process. There are three basic approaches to prevent this from happening. Sometimes the methods are used in combination.

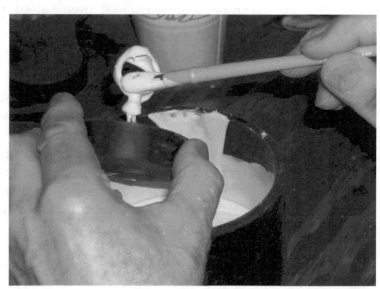

**Figure 6.1
Painting a layer of
investment on a wax
model to minimize air
bubbles**

As described earlier, the first step in eliminating bubbles is to use a wetting agent. Wetting agents are usually employed in addition to the other approaches that are used to minimize bubbles. Different types of wetting agents are used depending upon whether the investment is vacuumed or not.

In addition to using a wetting agent, one can paint a layer of investment directly on the model to further minimize the possibility that bubbles will become attached to the model. This is illustrated in Figure 6.1. Any bubbles that form should be broken with the brush while coating the model. After completing a bubble-free coating, the flask is pressed into the sprue base and the remaining investment is carefully poured into the flask. The two steps of coating a model with a wetting agent followed by a painted-on layer of investment can be very effective in eliminating bubbles; however, the process is time consuming and not well suited to commercial casting.

Figure 6.2 shows a typical vibrator that is used in another approach to bubble elimination. The bowl of investment is placed on the vibrator before pouring the investment into the flask. The vibration will

Figure 6.2
A typical vibrator that is used to shake bubbles loose in a bowl of investment (Photo courtesy of Grobet USA™)

cause the bubbles to rise to the surface of the investment where they will break and release air from the
investment. This minimizes the amount of air
trapped in the investment and, therefore, minimizes the number of bubbles that will become
attached to a model that has previously been coated
with a wetting agent. After pouring the investment
carefully into the flask, the complete flask and
model assembly is again vibrated to shake any
remaining bubbles loose from the model so they can
rise to the surface of the investment in the flask.
This technique is not 100 percent effective, although
satisfactory results may be obtained with experience. Some craftsmen used this technique exclu-
sively.

Vacuum debubblizing is the most satisfactory method

The final method for eliminating bubbles we will
call vacuum debubblizing. It is quite effective and is
usually used by commercial casters. It is particularly important when large trees of wax models
are invested, with the potential for trapping air
bubbles in the narrow spaces between models. Such
a trapped bubble may cause adjacent castings to
become attached to each other and may make the
castings useless. Globules of metal attached to castings may be removed, but this requires extra hand
cleanup work.

Vacuum debubblizing works on the principle that
all the minute bubbles of air in the investment will
expand in size when the bowl of investment is
placed in a vacuum. The larger bubbles will then
rise to the surface of the investment where they will
break, thus eliminating the air bubbles from the
investment. This is much more effective than simply using a vibrator. Vibrating the bowl slightly
while it is in the vacuum chamber helps even more
to dislodge the bubbles.

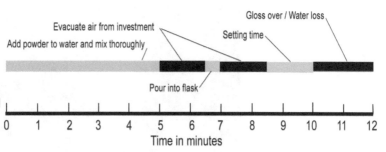

Figure 6.3
Timeline showing the steps in preparing and pouring investment into to a flask

Jewelery making or dental gypsum-based invest-ments set or solidify about nine minutes after the powder is added to the water. The time line shown in Figure 6.3 illustrates the time sequence for the above steps for an investment with a manufac-turer's specified working time of 9 minutes. The actual working time may be longer depending on the temperature and atmospheric pressure. Be sure to use a mixing bowl with about twice the volume of the investment being mixed so that it will not run over when it expands in the vacuum.

So-called *water streaking* sometimes occurs when the investment is poured into the flask too soon. This happens when water collects on the surface of the model and leaves a visible streak on the finished casting. The various steps performed while invest-ing a model should be timed so that the flask is filled with vacuumed investment just before seven minutes have elapsed. Just enough time should remain after pouring the investment for the flask to be placed in the bell jar and again vacuumed before the investment starts to set or solidify.

Filling the flask

After the thoroughly mixed investment has been vacuumed for the first time, carefully pour the

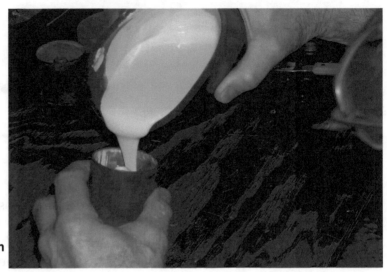

**Figure 6.4
Pouring investment
into a flask while
avoiding pouring it on
top of the model**

investment down the side of the flask as shown in
Figure 6.4 so that it will rise in the flask and cover
the model from below. Do not pour the investment
directly onto the model. Don't forget to put a rubber
flask extender on the flask or wrap some masking
tape around the top of the flask before pouring so
that the investment can expand about 25 percent
without overflowing. The remaining bubbles should
rise to top and the investment should fall back into
the flask just before nine minutes elapses.

Remove the vacuum just before the investment
starts to set at the end of nine minutes.

Vacuum debubblizing

The following steps are required for vacuum debubblizing:

1. Mix investment in bowl for about five minutes.

2. Place the bowl of investment in a vacuum bell, close
valves, and start the vacuum pump.

3. Wait while the investment forms lots of bubbles and
almost doubles in volume.

4. When the bubbles break and the volume of investment falls or contracts in the bowl, open the air valve to release the vacuum and turn off the vacuum pump.

5. Pour investment carefully into the flask, taking care not to pour directly on the model.

6. Place the flask with a flask extender back in the bell jar, close valves, and again turn on the vacuum pump.

7. Open valves and turn off the vacuum pump after the investment in the flask expands and then contracts.

8. The flask should be allowed to sit quietly, or be moved very carefully and set aside until the investment sets.

Setting time

The surface of the investment should gloss over just after nine minutes. That is, the surface will change from shiny to a dull or matte appearance. Don't disturb the flask (or else move it very carefully) until the investment has completely set in a few more minutes. It will continue to harden for another ten to fifteen minutes.

The invested flask should be allowed to sit for about one hour before starting burnout. The strength of the mold increases during this time. However, drying for a period of time greater than about two hours may cause other problems. If allowed to dry too much the mold may explode when burnout is started. The explosion is not too violent -- it just splatters a lot of investment throughout your oven. If the flask is kept moist it can be safely placed in a 1350° F (732° C) oven. The only time I have ever had one explode was when the investment was too viscous and voids that trapped steam were left in the investment.

If it is necessary to wait for more than a couple of hours, say overnight, the flask should be placed in a bucket with a wet rag thrown over it. A little water in the bottom of the bucket might help, too. The point of this is to keep the flask damp until it is placed in the burnout oven. A mold that has been allowed to dry too much should be placed in water to completely saturate the investment before oven burnout. Later we will discuss steam wax elimination prior to burnout. This also will produce a well-saturated flask.

Other techniques

The manual methods just described may be used to produce satisfactory molds. A simple vibrator may work well on occasion. However, vacuum outgassing is more successful for producing consistent results. For production work, methods and equipment have been developed so that the entire investment process from mixing the investment to filling the flask is carried out in a vacuum. This prevents air from becoming trapped in the investment during initial mixing and prevents air from being added to the investment as it is poured into the flask. Any small bubbles that may remain become microscopic when the vacuum is released before the investment hardens. Vacuum investment equipment produces consistent results when large flasks containing many models are invested.

Gypsum-based investments are produced by several companies in the United States and elsewhere. The formulations consist of a gypsum binder, combined with an additional refractory material such as pure silica or crystobolite, an alternative form of silicon dioxide. While the precise formulations are trade secrets, it is known that a number of components have been added to improve the characteristics of the investment. The addition of a wetting agent to the powdered investment is one example. Other agents have been added to try to remove oxygen from the mold following burnout to minimize oxidation of the metal as the casting is made.

When casting metals such as platinum and stainless steel, which melt above about 2000° F (1093° C), gypsum-based investment is not used, because the necessary high melting temperature causes the investment to weaken and rapidly break down into sulfur compounds that in turn combine with the cast metal. Some high-temperature investments harden into pure silica.

Recently, investment-casting specialists have developed a new technique called ceramic shell molds. Ceramic shell molds are created by repetitive dipping of the model to produce a thin investment coating that is then fired to produce a thin but strong ceramic shell. The thin shell makes it possible to complete the burnout in a very short period of time. While the repetitive dipping may extend the investment time, the burnout time period is greatly reduced when making large, massive castings. Modern investment-casting foundries use ceramic shell casting for a broad range of industrial products and sculpture, while traditional gypsum investment still dominates the jewelry and dental fields for gold and silver casting.

Advanced methods

While the methods just described will generally produce satisfactory results for small-scale investment casting, additional special considerations may be necessary in certain circumstances. Investment will expand and contract at different temperatures during the burnout process (described in the next chapter). Where extreme dimensional control is necessary, such as during certain dental casting, the effects of mold expansion and contraction must be controlled. Some dental casting textbooks and manufacturers' guidelines recommend lining the flask with a fiber sheet so that the mold can expand slightly to compensate for the slight model shrinkage that occurs when the wax model is made. These variations are of the order of a few percent and may be of no importance at other times. When extreme dimensional control is necessary, the manufacturer's recommendations should be followed for each brand of investment. The choice and amount of refractory filler in the investment affects its dimensional characteristics.

Special flask preparation

The use of a flask liner is just one of several extra preparations that must be made during the investment process. The use of very large flasks during commercial casting presents a problem of inadequate investment porosity. Several solutions to the porosity problem have been presented elsewhere; however, the particular solution may require modification of steps in the investment process. For example, perforated flasks require the use of a rubber sleeve or masking tape to cover the holes while the investment is liquid. If a wax web is placed within a solid flask to improve the resistance to airflow, it must be inserted into the flask before investing. These steps should be added to any checklist of investing steps. The full significance of these special considerations will become apparent as additional casting methods are introduced later in this book.

7

Wax Elimination

Overview

Wax elimination is usually called *burnout* because most people simply put casting flasks filled with hardened investment into a furnace or oven and start a heating process that lasts anywhere from 2 to 15 hours. Near the end of the process when the oven has reached a temperature of about 1350° F (732° C), the final remnants of wax have turned to carbon, which is, in turn, burned to a vapor. Table 7.1 illustrates several typical burnout cycles. No reasons are given for each step in the process, and there are many other alternative burnout sequences. Wax elimination is a step in the lost-wax process with many different recommendations, but few facts.

The overall concept of wax elimination is simple. Wait until the investment has hardened suffi-ciently, then: (1) heat the flask until the wax melts and runs out the sprue opening; (2) raise the flask temperature to about 1350° F (732° C) to vaporize all wax that may have been absorbed into the investment; (3) lower the temperature of the flask to what is called *flask casting temperature*, which depends on the metal and pattern being cast. The burnout cycle just described will always work for flasks up to 3-1/2 to 4 inches in diameter.

Table 7.1 Three typical burnout protocols

5-hour burnout	8-hour burnout	12-hour burnout
For flasks up to 2.5" x 2.5"	For flasks up to 3.5" x 4"	For flasks up to 4" x 8"
Preheat furnace to 300° F	Preheat furnace to 300° F	Preheat furnace to 300° F
1 hour -- 300° F	2 hours -- 300° F	2 hours -- 300° F
1 hour -- 700° F	2 hours -- 700° F	2 hours -- 600° F
2 hours -- 1350° F	3 hours -- 1350° F	2 hours -- 900° F
1 hour -- See note	1 hour -- See note	4 hours -- 1350° F
		2 hours -- See note

Note: During the last hour or two of burnout the temperature should be adjusted so that the flasks are the correct temperature for casting when removed from the oven.

A five-hour burnout cycle is recommended for smaller flasks and a 12-hour cycle is recommended for larger flasks. These burnout cycles will generally work, but there are also other burnout cycles that work just as well. In addition, many casters find it useful to eliminate most of the wax in a steam dewaxer before placing the flask in the oven. This results in a much less smelly burnout process because most of the wax has been drained from the mold before the flask is placed in the oven. Dental technicians may burn out a flask (which they call a *ring*) in about an hour. This is because dental castings are generally very small objects (crowns and inlays) and the ring is an inch (25mm) or less in diameter. It takes much less time to heat the small flask up to the wax-melting temperature and then to the final burnout temperature.

Burnout objectives

Let's examine some of the other variables that may be altered in the wax elimination process. Burnout for lost-wax casting has several objectives. The first objective is to eliminate the wax model and leave a cavity that will be used to cast a duplicate of the original model in metal.

The second objective is to eliminate all of the water that occupies the space surrounding the crystals of gypsum that form as the liquid investment hardens. This water turns to steam when the internal mold temperature rises above 212° F (100° C) and escapes from the flask. Some of the wax from the model may soak into the pores in the investment as the free water is vaporized.

Burnout makes the investment porous

A final burnout objective is to eliminate any wax from the pores in the investment so that gases can be forced out of the mold during the casting process. When properly "burned out" the investment becomes relatively permeable and the gases in the mold cavity can be forced out through the mold walls by the incoming molten metal during centrifugal casting, for example. As described in Chapter 5 (Figure 5.9), additional passageways may be added to larger flasks by including large vent sprues or by boring large holes in the walls of the flask to further reduce the resistance to gases being expelled through the investment. During vacuum-assisted casting, the gases are pulled out of the mold cavity through the investment and auxiliary passageways by a vacuum pump, and metal is forced into the mold by atmospheric pressure.

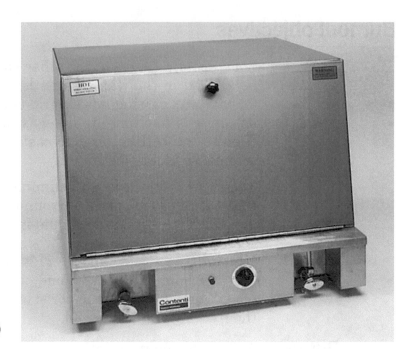

**Figure 7.1
A typical steam
dewaxer (Photo
courtesy of The
Contenti Company)**

Steam dewaxing

As suggested earlier, to avoid shop pollution, some
casters find it useful to eliminate most of the wax in
a mold using a steam dewaxer, such as the one
shown in Figure 7.1, before placing the flask in the
burnout oven. Steam dewaxers are available from
many suppliers; however, inexpensive alternatives
are available and are described in the chapter on
homemade equipment. One simply needs a container for the flask that will boil water and produce
steam that, in turn, heats the flask and melts most
of the wax in the sprues and mold cavity.

Because the steam is maintained at 212° F (100° C),
the wax is simply melted rather than vaporized.
The melted wax can be caught in a tray and recov-
ered for re-use if desired. When the flask is placed
in the burnout oven to raise it to a higher temperature there is only a small amount of wax left in the

pores of the investment and much less odor is released into the shop.

Achieving adequate burnout

Burnout is complete when the contents of a flask have been raised to 1350° F (732° C) for a period of time that is sufficient to eliminate all wax from the pores in the investment. The investment must be sufficiently porous for trapped gases to escape when metal is forced into the sprue system.

It is easy to tell when a flask has not been burned out sufficiently: a gray coating of carbonized wax remains over the entire pouring cup of a flask. When burnout is adequate the exposed surface of the investment will be chalky-white. Sometimes some stains or spots remain, but, in general, the pouring cup will turn from gray to chalky-white when burnout is complete. The process may take from one hour to several hours depending on the size of the flask and the number of flasks loaded into an oven.

Leave the oven door ajar during burnout! Partway through the burnout process, flasks that were initially sprue-downward should be turned over so that oxygen can reach the pouring cup to completely oxidize any remaining carbonized wax. A burnout oven cannot be sealed. Air (the oxygen in the air) is required to complete the burnout process. Leaving the oven door slightly ajar is usually sufficient.

The time necessary for adequate burnout must either be determined experimentally for various flask sizes and oven packing, or one must use the cookbook (more than adequate) burnout recommendations provided by investment manufacturers.

Traditional burnout

At the beginning of this chapter we showed several time-temperature profiles suitable for dewaxing flasks of various sizes. Any oven that can reach a temperature of about 1500° F is suitable. A look through any jeweler's supply catalog will reveal a variety of sizes. Some are heated with resistance wire elements that operate on ordinary 120 volt house power, while other larger ovens require special 240 volt wiring such as used by electric kitchen stoves. Other ovens are designed to operate on natural or bottled gas. Kilns designed for pottery firing are also suitable for burnout.

The main problem with "traditional burnout" is the length of the burnout cycle and the necessity of adjusting the oven temperature several times. At this point computers have come to the rescue and computer-operated *temperature controllers* are available to make the appropriate temperature adjustment throughout the burnout. Some controllers, such as shown in Figure 7.2, are external devices that may be attached to existing ovens while other controllers are built into the oven.

The digital temperature controllers are particularly useful in a commercial setting where burnout may be scheduled overnight so that flasks are ready to cast first thing in the morning. When using large flasks containing many models the final period of burnout may require two hours, and it is very convenient to have the controller reduce the oven to casting temperature during the early hours of the morning before employees arrive.

**Figure 7.2
A typical digital
temperature controller
that may be attached
to any oven (Photo
courtesy of The
Contenti Company)**

Fast burnout

It is also possible to place a moist flask into an oven
already heated to 1350° F (732° C). Then the complete burnout cycle can be very fast—a dental ring
in an hour and a medium-sized jewelry flask in two
to three hours instead of five hours.

The flask must be moist or it may crack, or even
explode. If a flask is allowed to dry for more than
about an hour after the investment hardens, the
exposed investment will start to dry out. It is the
partially dried flask that is subject to damage when
placed into a high-temperature oven.

During the rising temperature phase of any burnout
cycle the oven must be hotter than the flask for heat
to be transferred to the flask. The oven temperature
initially drops due to the cooling effect of the flask.
However, the oven temperature remains above the

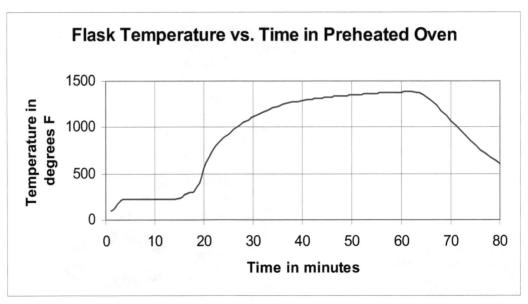

Figure 7.3   Flask temperature at center of a 2 x 2-1/2 inch flask after placing it in an oven adjusted to 1350° F

flask temperature, and heat is transferred to the flask. Eventually the flask temperature will rise almost to the oven temperature.

The temperature at the center of the flask rises to only about 212° F (100° C) during the first few minutes. Then the internal temperature of the flask will remain at the boiling point of water until all the free water is driven from the investment. Only when the wax is all melted out and the free water has been driven out will the flask temperature start to rise, regardless of the oven temperature. This is clearly shown in Figure 7.3. The time to dry the mold and then the time to reach the final burnout temperature are dependent on the size of the flask.

The maximum burnout temperature inside the mold should be above 1200° F to eliminate all carbon residues from the wax. Some of the wax will penetrate into the investment during the early part of the burnout and must be completely vaporized during the final stages of burnout. Most instructions recommend that the oven should be raised to 1350° F (732° C) for a time period that depends on the size of the flask. The maximum temperature of 1350° F should not be exceeded when using gypsum investment, because the plaster starts to degrade rapidly at higher temperatures.

After the flask has been maintained at maximum temperature long enough to vaporize all wax that has penetrated into the investment, the oven should be lowered to the final casting temperature. One does not generally cast while the flask is still at the maximum temperature, because the solidification of the metal in the mold will be delayed. If one is using a centrifugal casting machine it is possible for the metal to run back out of the mold when the revolving arm slows down and the centrifugal force is no longer sufficient to hold the metal in the mold.

There are some ancient casting methods, such as Ashanti casting, where a clay mold is raised above the melting point of the metal and casting is done while the mold is above the melting point of the metal (see Chapter 10). Then the mold and casting are not disturbed until the temperature has dropped sufficiently to be sure that the metal is completely solidified.

Based on a number of experiments, we can recommend that burnout times seldom exceed four hours when a single moderate-sized flask is placed in a preheated oven. There is little difference between the time-temperature profile of a flask where the wax has been eliminated by steam and where the wax is melted during the first part of the oven burnout. The burnout cycles recommended are primarily a function of the size of the flask, which, in turn, determines the time it takes to eliminate the free water and the time it takes for the flask to rise to maximum temperature. It is important to remember that several flasks placed in an oven at one time will take longer to burnout than a single flask placed in the oven at the same temperature. The total thermal mass of several flasks is greater than a single flask so, in effect, several small flasks require a total burnout time equivalent to a single much larger flask.

Benefits of fast burnout

We have used the term *fast burnout* to describe the burnout procedure starting with an oven already heated to over 1350° F (732° C). There are several advantages to using this technique. In addition to a faster total burnout time, we have found that burnout using this approach does not produce a lot of smoke or a strong wax smell in the shop. The wax appears to carbonize and the carbon is eliminated by immediate conversion to carbon dioxide, a colorless, odorless gas. Usually the wax smell is rather pervasive during conventional burnout in spite of hoods and exhaust fans.

Fast burnout is great for classroom demonstration Another advantage in a teaching environment is that the fast burnout cycle allows a student to design a wax model, invest, burnout, and cast in a single day. Investing, burnout, and casting can be completed in as few as three hours when the flask is small. Thus it is possible to spend a morning on a wax design project, start burnout over the lunch hour, cast by mid-afternoon, and complete the finishing before the day is over. I often use the fast burnout procedure in the classroom for demonstrations.

It should be noted that an oven full of 20-30 small student flasks is not suitable for a fast burnout. The thermal mass of a large number of small flasks is more suitable for overnight burnout. This can be done with an oven without a digital temperature controller by simply determining the setting of the manual control that will hold 1350° F (732° C) for the rest of the night. The flasks should all be turned over after most of the wax has melted out to be sure that air can reach the sprue openings and permit a complete burnout.

8

Vacuum-Assisted Casting

Casting, in general

Casting is the final step in the lost-wax process. Once a mold has been burned out, all that is left to do is pour metal into the mold, and we have a reproduction of the original wax model. However, this step is not as simple as it sounds. First, there are several alternative means of forcing metal into the mold. Then, there are a number of problems that must be overcome.

At least in concept, all we need to do is remove a burned-out flask from the furnace, set it on a firebrick, and pour molten metal into the pouring cup. This would be called gravity casting, because the weight of the molten metal would force some metal into the mold. Unfortunately, this doesn't always work very well. The air and gases in the mold keep the metal from entering, and we would have only a partially filled mold, at best.

Sculptors overcome this problem by adding vents to the sprue system so that air and gases can escape when metal enters the pouring cup and starts to flow into the mold.

Safety glasses and gloves should be worn when working with hot metal!

As pointed out earlier, investment molds for jewelry and dental castings are made of material that becomes somewhat porous during burnout. If one simply poured metal into the pouring cup, some gases would be forced out through the pores in the investment by the weight of the metal in the pouring cup and sprues. But this would still not work very well. A better solution is to place the flask on a piece of equipment that uses a pump to suck the gases out of the mold. Then gravity and atmospheric pressure will force the metal into the mold. This is called vacuum-assisted casting, which is described first because the vacuum pump needed for vacuuming investment will also work for vacuum-assisted casting.

Pre-casting preparation

The first step in casting (using any casting method) is to weigh an appropriate amount of metal pellets, called casting grain. Casting grain is generally the form in which precious metals are received from a refiner or supplier. The pellets are easier to weigh precisely than larger pieces of metal or bullion.

If scrap gold or sprues and buttons from a previous cast are to be used, about 50 percent new casting grain should be used for the best results. This is because the casting grain supplied by a refiner contains small amounts of additives in the alloy that may be burned out or vaporized during the melting process. For example, small amounts of zinc may be added to an alloy to improve the fluidity of the melt. Because zinc melts at a considerably lower temperature than gold or silver, some of the zinc will vaporize during the melting process, thus changing the composition of the alloy in the buttons and sprues. This is the reason that scrap gold may not be the best alloy for casting. In addition, care should be taken to eliminate any solder that may be present in scrap gold. Most scrap gold chain should not be used for casting because the links may not be solid and may instead contain a solder core. Solder and other impurities in scrap gold are often the cause of poor casting results.

Don't forget to weigh the model before burnout. Usually one would weigh casting metal during the burnout phase because a number of hours must elapse while all wax is eliminated from the investment. The weight of metal to be used is equal to the weight of the wax model and sprue system plus ten percent, multiplied by the specific gravity of the metal being used. This formula usually works properly because wax has a specific gravity of about 1.0. Multiplying the weight of the wax by the specific gravity of the metal gives a result that will fill the mold cavity and the sprue system, with enough extra to produce a little button in the bottom of the pour cup formed by the sprue base. The button provides a reservoir of molten metal to fill the mold completely and adds the mass of the button to the forces that push the metal into the mold.

The formula just described may not work very well if one is casting a single, very light lady's ring, for example. If the wax model weighs a fraction of a gram, it may be more satisfactory to add 25 or 50, or even 100 percent to the calculated weight of metal. The important point is to have a button of sufficient size to remain molten and supply metal while the casting solidifies.

It is customary to calculate the amount of metal required when the wax is weighed before investing so that the weight of metal can be recorded in a notebook or written or scratched into the end of the invested flask. This is particularly important if several flasks are processed at one time or if different persons are handling various steps of the overall casting process. A separate record of the amounts of metal needed should be kept so that the metal can be weighed during the burnout phase, as just suggested. The weighed casting grain should be placed in appropriately marked plastic bags, or other containers, to await casting.

Vacuum-assisted casting

Vacuum-assisted casting is one of the two most common methods used for jewelry and dental casting. The other method is centrifugal casting, which will be described in the next chapter. Experts debate the merit of one method over the other. The term *vacuum casting* is sometimes applied to a casting method where the complete casting process is carried out in a vacuum. However, here I will use the term vacuum-assisted casting to denote a casting technique where a vacuum pump is used to exhaust the gases within an invested flask. Then atmospheric pressure (around 14 pounds per square inch) is used to force metal into the mold cavity.

If one has a vacuum pump and bell jar to remove air from investment during the investing phases of lost-wax casting, little more equipment is required to perform vacuum-assisted casting. In fact, most vacuum outfits sold for vacuuming investment also include the components required for vacuum

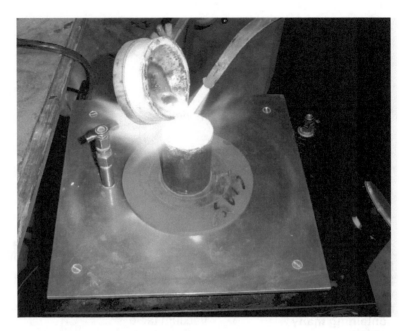

**Figure 8.1
Vacuum-assisted
casting.
Photo courtesy of
Steve C. Birkes.**

assisted casting. Basically, all one needs is a casting table, such as shown in Figure 8.1, with a high-temperature silicon-rubber pad on which a hot flask may be set. The opening of a pipe attached to the vacuum pump is in the middle of the rubber pad so that the flask may be set over the hole. When the pump is turned on, all the air and gas is pumped out of the mold. Normally, more air will be drawn into the sprue hole. If molten metal is poured into the pouring cup in the flask just as the pump is turned on, the metal, instead of air, will enter the mold under the force of atmospheric pressure.

The setup just described works satisfactorily when using small flasks containing one or two models. However, a larger flask containing a tree with many waxes on it may cast incompletely.

This can be understood by looking at Figure 8.2. Note the models that are far up the trunk of the tree near the pouring cup are more isolated from the vacuum that is pulled at the bottom end of the flask

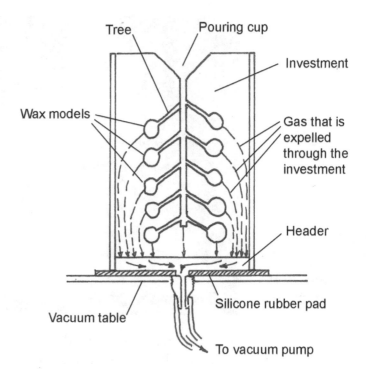

Tree Pouring cup

Investment

Wax models

Gas that is
expelled
through the
investment

Header

Silicone rubber pad

Vacuum table

To vacuum pump

Figure 8.2
Long air pathways
when vacuum casting
a large flask and tree
containing many
models.

Because there is a longer path through the investment to the header at the bottom of the flask, the
gases will be drawn from the upper models more
slowly, and incomplete filling may result

To reduce the resistance to airflow, a wax grid is
sometimes used to line the flask. This produces
additional air passages after it is melted out during
burnout. The wax grid must not project above the
flask near the pouring cup or leaking air will
destroy the effectiveness of this approach.

Another method of making the vacuum system
more effective on large flasks is to perforate the
flask as shown in Figure 8.3. In this case, the flask
projects into a vacuum chamber with a silicon-rubber seal around the flange. All the holes in the flask
greatly reduce the resistance to airflow, and all the
models throughout a large flask will be evacuated.

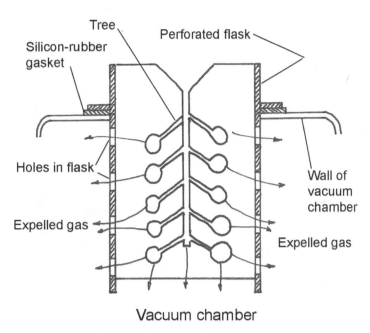

Tree

Silicon-rubber gasket

Perforated flask

Holes in flask

Wall of vacuum chamber

Expelled gas

Expelled gas

Figure 8.3
Large perforated flask
with minimized
resistance to air flow.

Vacuum chamber

Melting the metal

For vacuum-assisted casting the metal may be melted by any of several methods. The simplest in concept is a melting pot similar to the one shown in Figure 8.4. Casting grain is placed in the carbon crucible in the pot, and the electric power is turned on. A pyrometer indicates the metal temperature and shows when the proper pouring temperature has been reached. Automated melting pots are available that regulate the temperature of the melt.

When the molten metal is ready to pour, the flask (held at the proper pouring temperature) is removed from the oven and set on the silicone rubber pad over the hole with the pour cup facing upwards. Turn on the vacuum pump, and make sure the base of the flask is sealed by noting whether the indica-

**Figure 8.4
Kerr® Electro-Melt™
Furnace for melting
casting grain.**

tor on the vacuum pump shows a vacuum of at least
25 inches of mercury. Then quickly pour the
required amount of metal into the mold.

It is easy to overflow the pour cup if the melting pot
contains molten metal for several flasks. A better
approach is to melt only sufficient metal for the particular flask.

Vacuum-assisted casting requires the minimum
amount of equipment for quality casting. No torches
are required -- only a burnout oven, a vacuum pump
both for removing air from the investment and for
casting, and a melting pot. Vacuum-assisted casting
seems to appeal to inexperienced persons because
the final stages of casting are less complicated and a
minimum amount of coordination is required to
remove the flask from the oven and pour the metal.

Open-crucible torch melting

A torch may be used to melt metal in open crucibles,
as shown in Figure 8.5, if appropriate melting

**Figure 8.5
Torch melting using
an open crucible.**

torches are available. Large torch tips, so-called TurboTorches®, or multi-orifice "rosebud" torch tips should be used to rapidly melt the metal.

Some preparation is required for open-crucible torch melting. The hand crucible, such as shown in Figure 8.5, is usually received un-prepared for melting metal. Before it can be used, the inner surface of the crucible must be coated with melted borax. This is done by melting borax powder with a torch in the crucible. The molten borax looks like glass and is spread around the crucible depression by tipping the crucible so it will flow over the entire surface. In general, to prevent contamination, it is worthwhile to prepare separate crucibles for gold and silver or any other metal being melted.

Once prepared, a crucible may be used to melt casting grain that is then poured into the pouring cup of a flask. New casting grain as received from a metal supplier generally melts easily with no further attention. Scrap or previously used metal may require additional fluxing with borax to remove impurities from the melt. One simply sprinkles a pinch of borax powder on top of a pool of molten metal that is then stirred with a glass or carbon rod to pick up the impurities. Remove the contaminated borax flux with the stirring rod and discard. When the pool of molten metal is clean and mirror-like, turn on the vacuum pump and pour into the pouring cup of the flask.

Alternative methods

Homemade equipment may also be constructed to take advantage of the features of vacuum-assisted casting. A manual pump, such as shown in Figure 15.3, can be used to remove air from the mold when the metal is poured. A similar plunger-type device has been shown in magazines for hobby casting.

Condensing steam can also be used to create a vacuum for casting. This works on the principle that was used to develop the first steam engine. A small amount of water is placed in a spherical chamber. It is heated over a flame and the opening in the sphere is closed with a stopper. Rapidly cooling the sphere and the steam produces a vacuum in the sphere, which may be used for vacuum casting. With practice, consistent results are possible.

Step-by-step vacuum-assisted casting

(using a melting pot)

The following casting steps follow the burnout described in Chapter 7. The instructions are based on the use of a Kerr® Standard Electro-Melt™ furnace to melt the casting grain. When using the Electro-Melt™ pot, the vacuum table should be set on a platform so that the silicon-rubber pad is lower than waist-high. It is difficult to pour metal from a melting pot if the flask is at standard table height.

1. If desired, set burnout oven to final flask casting temperature one-half to one hour before casting. We have found that satisfactory castings using small flasks can be obtained without reducing the oven temperature before casting. This is useful in a classroom setting where the burnout furnace is maintained at a single temperature throughout the burnout process as described in the last chapter. Simply remove the flask and set aside for a few minutes until it cools to an appropriate casting temperature.

2. Place pre-measured casting grain in melting pot. Record the weight: _____

3. Turn melting pot on by setting the power-control switch to "HI" about 20 minutes before the flask in the burnout oven will be ready to cast.

4. After about 15 minutes, set power-control switch to 6.2 when the pyrometer indicates that the crucible has reached 1500° F. (Do not allow temperature to exceed 1500° F with the power-control switch set on "HI".)

5. Select the proper metal casting temperature from Appendix D for the alloy being cast or, better yet, use the casting temperature recommended by the manufacturer for the specific alloy being used.

6. Set the power-control switch to the setting shown in Electro-Melt™ manual that corresponds to proper metal casting temperature shortly before the melting reaches that temperature.

7. When the metal is melted, stir with a carbon rod to be sure the metal is thoroughly melted and to remove any impurities. Flux is not generally required because the carbon rod will pick up impurities.

8. When the metal is at casting temperature, remove flask from the burnout oven with tongs and place it over the vacuum hole on the red silicon-rubber casting pad with the sprue opening facing upwards.

9. Turn on vacuum pump and close the valve to apply vacuum to flask.

Take care to not splash molten metal on yourself!

10. Turn off the casting pot and pour metal into the flask pour cup.

11. After 10 to 15 seconds, when the button has solidified, open the valve to release the vacuum and then turn off the vacuum pump.

12. To minimize damage to the red silicon-rubber casting pad, remove the hot flask with tongs and set it aside on a fireproof surface to cool.

13. When the button no longer shows a red glow in dim light, use tongs to slowly lower the flask into a bucket of water. It will boil and bubble. Do not wait too long or steam will not be generated to break up the investment surrounding the casting.

14. Remove the cast object from flask or bottom of the bucket and clean off the loosened investment with an old toothbrush.

15. Place object in a pot of hot pickling solution to remove the remaining investment and any surface oxide or sulfide coating.

Step-by-step vacuum-assisted casting

(using a melting torch)

1. Remove flask from the oven and set it on a metal surface adjacent to the silicon-rubber high-temperature casting pad on the vacuum caster.

2. Place pre-measured casting grain in melting crucible. Record the weight: _____

3. It is probably desirable to maintain separate crucibles for gold, silver, and brass because some metal may remain in the crucible and contaminate a different alloy.

4. Melt the metal with a high-heat torch.

5. When the metal melts, swirl in the crucible to clean the metal with the flux already on the crucible.

6. Add flux, if necessary, and stir with a carbon rod to pick up impurities.

7. When the metal is melted, place the crucible on the silicon-rubber pad over the hole in the vacuum table.

8. Turn on the vacuum pump.

9. Note whether the flask is sealed against the rubber pad by an indicated vacuum of at least 25 inches of mercury.

10. Lift crucible to pouring position with the right hand (or dominant hand) while keeping the torch on the molten metal.

11. Start to tip the crucible while heating both the molten metal and the lip of the crucible so that the metal will not solidify on the edge of the crucible.

12. Pour in one rapid motion as the torch flame is removed from the molten metal. Do not hesitate!

13. Vacuum should immediately draw metal into the mold.

14. After the button solidifies, release the vacuum from the system and then turn off the vacuum pump.

15. To minimize damage to the silicon-rubber pad, remove the flask and set it aside to cool on a metal surface or firebrick.

16. When the button no longer shows a red glow in dim light, use tongs to slowly lower the flask into a bucket of water.

17. Remove the cast object from flask or bottom of the bucket and clean off the loosened investment with an old toothbrush.

18. Place the object in a hot pickle pot to remove the remaining investment and any surface oxide or sulfide coating.

9

Centrifugal Casting

Technique

As indicated earlier, metal must be injected into a mold with considerable force, which in turn causes any gases trapped in the mold to be expelled through the very small pores of the hardened investment. The means of generating the force for injecting metal into the mold identifies the casting method. Centrifugal casting utilizes forces generated when the flask is rapidly rotated. Centrifugal force "slings" the metal into the mold. When dentists first started casting gold crowns for patients, a flask was swung overhead at the end of a chain to create the centrifugal force.

Many dental technicians now use spring-powered centrifugal casting machines for making crowns and inlays. Manufacturing jewelers who cast large flasks containing many items attached to a large tree will use larger, more massive (and expensive) spring-wound casting machines or somewhat automated, motor-driven casting machines. Some mass-production manufacturing jewelers prefer vacuum casting equipment, as was described in the last chapter

Centrifugal casters

Some centrifugal casting machines have a straight arm while some have what is called a "broken arm." Figure 9.1 shows a broken-arm casting machine. Note how the arm is hinged so that the crucible and

**Figure 9.1
Small broken-arm
casting machine
mounted in a wash
tub.**

flask is at right angles to the axis of the casting arm. This allows the force on the metal in the crucible to be aimed directly into the flask when the arm is first released and the forces of acceleration are greater than the centrifugal forces. When the arm is moving fast enough the broken-arm segment will swing around to line up with the rest of the arm and the centrifugal force will be directed outward along the arm from the central pivot point. Some broken-arm centrifugal casting machines have a cam to push the broken arm out into alignment with the rest of the arm. At any rate, the centrifugal force generated by the rotating arm will throw the molten metal from the crucible into the pouring cup of the invested flask.

Spring-powered centrifugal casting machines are also manufactured with a straight arm such as shown in Figure 9.2. With this type of machine the force on the molten metal in the crucible is not directly into the pouring cup of the flask when the arm first starts to accelerate. However, straight-

Figure 9.2
Small straight-arm
casting machine.

arm machines function satisfactorily when operated by a sufficiently powerful spring. One might question the necessity of the more complicated mechanism in the broken-arm machines.

Centrifugal casting machines generally have a movable weight that is used to counterbalance the flask to prevent extreme vibration during casting. Balancing must be done prior to burnout or by using an invested flask of the same size that will be used for casting. If the weight of metal to be cast is significant, place an equivalent amount of casting grain in the crucible. This will shift into the flask during the casting process and will change the balance, but probably not by a significant amount.

Do not forget to balance the casting arm. The arm must be balanced by loosening the nut that holds the arm to the spring base. The arm will usually tip slightly one way or the other. Adjust the position of the weight until the arm balances. If a broken-arm machine is being balanced, place the arm in its extended position before balancing. If the weight is locked into position with a pin or screw that fits in one of several discrete holes, it may not be possible to obtain an exact balance. Merely lock the weight in the nearest position and re-tighten the nut that holds the arm on the spring base. If all flasks are the same size and weight, the balance weight can be left in one position and the balancing procedure need not be performed before each cast.

The steps used to cast a small flask with a spring-powered centrifugal casting machine will be described here. It will be noted if one rotates the arm of a centrifugal casting machine that rotation in one direction winds up a spring in the base. Usually two or three complete rotations are used to wind the spring sufficiently. Depending on the machine, a little pin or lever will be used to lock the arm with the spring wound. Releasing the pin by rotating the arm against the spring slightly performs the actual casting. Then the arm is released so that it can rotate rapidly and sling the molten metal into the mold. One should experiment with a cold casting machine before attempting an actual cast.

Before casting, it is generally recommended that the flask must be cooled to casting temperature for about an hour. Most texts recommend that massive silver pieces should be cast at 800° F while fine filigree or small parts should be cast at 900° or 1000° F. These "rules of thumb" are based on the fact that massive components solidify more slowly than fine filigree and it is possible that the centrifuge could slow down before the metal in the mold has solidified and the metal will run back out of the mold. It is desirable to have the metal solidify while the centrifugal force is still forcing metal into the mold.

The mold casting temperature is also a function of the alloy being cast. Some of the newer casting alloys may require a mold temperature that is different from the above rule-of-thumb. In a teaching environment with many small 2 x 2-1/2-inch flasks to cast, I regularly take the flask out of a 1350° F oven and put them in the casting machine for a short period of time while the metal is being melted. The flask temperature is not carefully controlled and is probably around 1000° F. Determining the optimum casting temperature may require some experimentation for different objects.

Torch melting

Once the flask has reached the proper casting temperature, some degree of coordination is required to melt the metal, place the flask in the casting machine, and release the arm at the proper time. Some help from a second person may be desirable. Because the flask starts to cool when it is removed from the burnout oven, it may be necessary to minimize the time the flask is in the casting machine. Preheating the metal and crucible before taking the

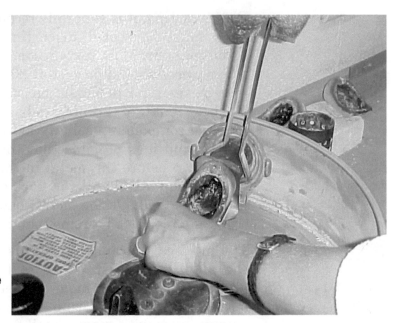

Figure 9.3
Placing a flask in the
Neycraft casting
machine.

flask out of the burnout oven can do this. Alternatively, the flask can be removed from the burnout oven at a temperature a little above the desired casting temperature. Experiments with a 2 x 2-1/2 inch flask have demonstrated that it takes a few minutes for the core temperature of the flask to drop 100° F. Adjust your working time accordingly.

Place the burned out flask in the casting machine as shown in Figure 9.3. Place pre-weighed casting grain in the crucible and melt with a torch. Air-gas torches will take longer to melt a given mass of metal than an oxygen-gas torch. Two air-gas torches may be required to melt a large mass of metal. The TurboTorch® is an air-acetylene torch that achieves higher temperatures by swirling air as it enters the torch. The 3/4-inch Turbo-torch shown in Figure 9.4 will quickly melt ounces of silver without the use of oxygen. Some experimentation may be required depending on the available equipment.

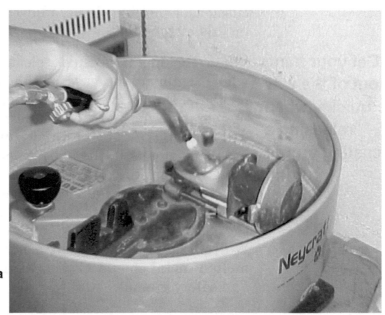

**Figure 9.4
Melting the metal in a
Neycraft casting
machine**

Remember that we mentioned in the last chapter
that when the metal is melted it may be necessary
to sprinkle a powdered flux on the metal to clean up
any oxides and impurities in the melt. For torch
melting the flux is usually powdered borax and only
a pinch is needed to produce a nice clean fluid mass
of metal. More may be required if the metal is old
and oxidized.

When melting metal with an oxygen-gas torch, it is
important not to turn on too much oxygen. Such an
oxidizing flame will form a scum on the metal surface that must be removed before casting. For torch
melting a reducing flame is desirable. Increasing
the gas flow relative to the oxygen flow until a distinct cone of unburned gas can be seen in the torch
flame creates a reducing flame. The bright inner
cone of flame closest to the torch tip is held above
the metal and the unburned gas beyond it protects
the metal from oxygen and keeps oxides from forming on the melted surface. For a more complete dis-

cussion of melting flame adjustment see any good metalsmithing text.

Get your hand out of the way quickly when releasing a casting arm or drum!

When the metal is fluid release the arm or the whole drum in the case of the Neycraft® casting machine. Do not overheat the metal or hold at high temperature for an extended period of time, as this will change the alloy by vaporizing the lower melting point metals in the alloy. Some care is required to manipulate the torch, load the flask, and release the arm without getting burned. Practice this beforehand with a cool flask to learn how to release the locking pin and get your hand out of the way. We remind you again that a person working near molten metal should always wear protective gloves and safety glasses.

The centrifuge arm should be allowed to rotate for several minutes and coast to a stop. If the arm is stopped too soon, still molten metal may run out of the flask and damage the casting. Remove the flask with tongs and set on a fireproof surface until the metal in the sprue button ceases to glow red in a dim light. (Larger flasks will take longer to cool than small flasks.) Then plunge the flask into a bucket of water to break up the investment and release the casting. The cool water will anneal the metal and make it ready for later processing steps.

Step-by-step centrifugal casting

(using a torch)

1. If necessary, set burnout oven to final flask casting temperature one-half to one hour before casting.

2. If not performed before burnout, balance centrifuge using a similar flask to the one in burnout.

3. Wind the centrifuge two or three revolutions and cock the broken arm, if present. Lock the arm in wound position.

4. Place pre-weighed casting grain in the crucible on the arm of the centrifuge.
Record the weight: _____

5. When flask is at proper casting temperature, remove from oven with tongs and place in the cradle of the casting machine. Lock crucible in position.

6. Quickly melt metal with a reducing flame. Excess gas will prevent the metal from being oxidized.

7. If necessary, add flux and stir with a carbon rod to remove any impurities.

8. When the metal is fluid as indicated by a shiny swirling surface, release the arm with a gloved hand.

9. Allow centrifuge to coast to a stop.

10. Remove flask from centrifuge and set on a fireproof surface to cool.

11. When the button no longer shows a red glow in dim light, use tongs to slowly lower the flask into a bucket of water.

12. When the flask stops bubbling and foaming, which breaks up the investment, remove the cast object from the flask or bottom of the bucket.

13. Remove the loosened investment with an old toothbrush. Be careful not to scratch the object if you must use a probe to remove some of the investment.

14. Place object in a hot pickle pot to remove the remaining investment and any surface coating.

15. When clean, remove from pickle pot and cutoff sprue(s). The object is now ready to finish.

Figure 9.5
JelenkoThermotrol®
straight-arm casting
machine with an
electrically heated
muffle furnace on the
arm

Electric furnace melting

We have just described the steps for casting with a simple spring-powered centrifugal casting machine using a torch for melting the metal. More sophisticated equipment is available that does not require the use of a torch. The Jelenko Thermotrol®, shown in Figure 9.5, has an electrically heated muffle furnace mounted on the centrifuge arm of the casting machine. The temperature of the melted metal is indicated by a built-in pyrometer. One simply heats the furnace, adds casting grain when the furnace is 400 degrees below the desired casting temperature, and then the arm is released when the proper temperature is reached. The actual casting temperature is significantly above the melting point of the casting grain alloy and is specified in literature accompanying the casting machine.

For large volume commercial applications, motor-driven centrifugal casting machines are available with built-in induction or resistive electric furnaces for heating large crucibles of metal. These machines generally include pyrometers for continuous temperature indication. One simply watches the temperature of the melting metal and switches on the centrifuge drive motor when the temperature is correct.

Other designs are possible that use centrifugal force to cast. Platinum centrifugal casting machines are available that accelerate the flask in a vertical rather than a horizontal plane. Home-built centrifugal casting machines have been described that use electric motors or a pull rope to accelerate the centrifuge.

Step-by-step centrifugal casting

(using a Thermotrol® caster)

1. If necessary, set burnout oven to final flask casting temperature one-half to one hour before casting.

2. If not performed before burnout, balance the centrifuge using a similar flask to the one in burnout.

3. Wind the centrifuge two or three revolutions and lock arm in wound position.

4. Follow instructions that come with the machine about pre-heating the melting furnace and bringing it up to casting temperature.

5. Watch the meter that continually monitors the temperature of the furnace.

6. Weigh the casting grain while the furnace is heating. Record the weight: _____

7. When the furnace temperature is 400° F below the alloy casting temperature, place pre-weighed

casting grain in the furnace on the centrifuge arm.

8. Remove the flask from the burnout oven with tongs and mount it on the arm of the casting machine.

9. Add a little special melting flux to the casting grain in the furnace on the arm.

10. When the melting furnace reaches the casting temperature, release the arm.

11. Allow centrifuge to coast to a stop.

12. Remove flask from centrifuge and set on a fire-proof surface to cool.

13. When the button no longer shows a red glow in dim light, use tongs to slowly lower the flask into a bucket of water.

14. Use care, as a massive object may still be hot.

15. When the flask stops bubbling and foaming, which breaks up the investment, remove the cast object from the flask or bottom of the bucket.

16. Remove most of the investment with an old toothbrush. Be careful not to scratch the object if you must use a probe to remove some of the investment.

17. Place object in a hot pickle pot to remove the remaining investment and any surface coating.

18. When clean, remove from pickle pot and cutoff sprue(s). The object is now ready for surface finishing.

10

Pressure and Steam Casting

Pressure casting

Air pressure or steam pressure may be used to force metal into a mold. In fact, commercially manufactured air-pressure casting systems are shown in textbooks of dental technology. At one time air pressure casting machines could be found in catalogs but they are not common now. Homemade designs are presented in some of the older casting books. To use the air-pressure approach to casting, proper spruing must have been prepared before investing the model to permit metal to be melted in the crucible depression made in the end of an invested flask.

Special sprues for air pressure and steam casting were shown in Chapter 5, Figure 5.5. The flask is invested in the normal way using the special three-prong sprue. When the sprue base is removed the pouring cup is enlarged with a spoon or spatula to make a crucible so that metal may be melted in the depression. This is shown in the cross-sectional dia-

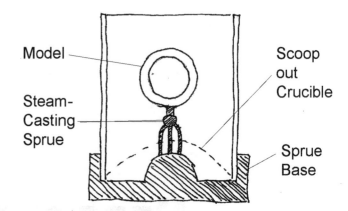

Model

Steam-
Casting
Sprue

Scoop
out
Crucible

Sprue
Base

Figure 10.1
Preparing an invested
flask for steam or
pressure casting.

gram in Figure 10.1. The 3-prong sprue is designed
to allow the metal to melt in the crucible without
running down into the mold. If the prongs are about
1 mm in diameter (or 14-gauge), the surface tension
of the molten metal will keep it in the crucible until
air or steam pressure is used to force the metal
through the narrow sprues into the wider sprue and
into the mold. It is also possible to make a single
wide flat sprue out of 14-gauge sheet wax with the
same effect.

Figure 10.2 shows metal being melted in the crucible scooped into the end of an invested flask. When

Figure 10.2
Melting metal in the
crucible scooped in
the end of a flask.

the metal is sufficiently fluid, a cap is pressed against the top of the flask and air pressure (between 10 and 15 pounds per square inch) is released by a valve to force the metal into the mold.

Other approaches to air-pressure casting have been devised. One very simple design involves a hand-operated tool that is essentially a spring-loaded plunger and a pressure cap that is placed over a flask containing molten metal, as illustrated in Figure 10.3. After a seal is produced the spring is

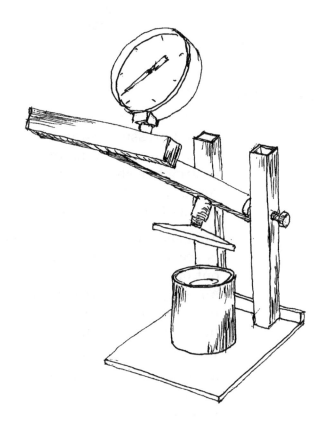

Figure 10.3
A pressure casting tool found in an old casting booklet. Sopcak, 1968.

released and the plunger compresses air on top of the molten metal. The metal is, in turn, forced into the mold, driving any trapped gas out through the pores in the investment.

**Figure 10.4
Home-made tool for
steam casting.**

Steam casting

Steam pressure using a home-made tool may also be used to drive the metal into the mold. The steam-casting tool shown in Figure 10.4 is pressed onto the top of a flask so that the molten metal heats the water-soaked material in the tool to produce steam.

To demonstrate the effectiveness of this approach, it is recommended that a steam-casting tool be made out of a piece of broom handle or wooden dowel and an old jar top. Press some paper toweling into the top and saturate with water. Shake off any water not absorbed by the toweling.

When ready to cast, take the burned-out flask from a burnout oven, set it over the gap between two fire-bricks, as shown in Figure 10.5, and melt the metal in the self-contained crucible. When the metal is melted, move the torch aside and clamp the steam-casting tool containing the water-soaked toweling over the flask. Press hard to keep the steam produced trapped in the cavity above the melted metal. Hold for several seconds to keep pressure on the

Figure 10.5
Setting burned out
flask over gap
between firebricks in
preparation for steam
casting.

metal until it solidifies. Some exposed edges of
paper towel may dry out and become scorched. If it
catches fire simply remove the fixture and press
against a piece of sheet metal to smother the
flames.

When the casting tool is removed from the flask, it
should be evident that the volume of metal in the
crucible is less than before and that molten metal
has been forced into the mold simultaneously forcing any trapped gases out through the pores in the
hardened investment. When the flask and casting
has cooled sufficiently lower the flask into a bucket
of water to break up the investment so that the
casting can be retrieved.

Steam casting is a simple, inexpensive method of
forcing metal into a mold. With experience, consistent results can be obtained. By using charcoal or a
hot plate for burnout, a very inexpensive casting
setup can be created.

Step-by-step steam casting

1. When at casting temperature, moisten several layers of paper towel in the steam-casting tool.

2. Remove flask from burnout oven and set over the gap between two hard firebricks.

3. Place pre-weighed casting grain in a crucible formed in the investment. Weight:_____

4. Melt casting grain with a torch.

5. Add a small amount of borax flux if the melted metal is not clean and shiny.

6. When molten and the top of the molten metal swirls, remove torch and quickly clamp the steam-casting tool over the flask.

7. Press the steam-casting tool tightly against the top of the flask to contain the steam generated by the water absorbed in the paper.

8. After a minute or so, remove the steam-casting tool and observe the button. It should be significantly smaller.

9. When the button no longer shows a red glow in dim light, use tongs to lower the flask into a bucket of water which breaks up the investment.

10. When the flask stops bubbling and foaming, remove the cast object from the flask or bottom of the bucket. (Use care, as a massive object may still be hot.)

11. Remove most of the loose investment with an old toothbrush. Be careful not to scratch the object if you must use a probe to remove some of the investment.

12. Place object in a hot pickle pot to remove the remaining investment and any surface coating.When clean, remove from pickle pot and cut off the sprue(s).

11

Ashanti Casting

Introduction

Ashanti casting is a primitive lost-wax casting technique still practiced by metalsmiths in Ghana on the Gold Coast of Africa. Besides being a window through which we can look back at ancient methods, Ashanti casting has several distinct advantages over conventional centrifugal or vacuum casting techniques. Because it is a primitive technique, only simple and inexpensive tools are necessary. Also, the Ashanti technique is useful when larger objects must be cast, or when pure silver, very thin sections, or hollow objects are desired. Each of these requirements is difficult to accomplish using conventional methods common among jewelers.

Ashanti casting is a gravity casting technique that involves no high-tech equipment. The craftsmen in Ghana base the technique described below on methods that have been in use for centuries. A Swiss jeweler, Max Frohlich, developed the specific methods after observing the Gold Coast craftsmen at work. I learned the complete process from Paulette Werger, a protégé of Frohlich, who uses the technique in her own work and is actively teaching others at workshops throughout the United States. Her approach is described in some detail in an article in *Metalsmith*. Any modifications that have been introduced here are the responsibility of this author.

Traditional Ashanti craftsmen used beeswax for making models.

The overall approach to Ashanti casting can be described briefly. A model is constructed using beeswax, which is then encased in a clay shell. After melting the wax from the mold by placing the invested object near a fire or glowing charcoal, a crucible containing unmelted casting metal is attached to the pouring cup of the mold with clay, and the whole mold and crucible are encased in additional clay. After the mold is allowed to air dry, the complete mold and crucible assembly with crucible on the bottom is placed in a charcoal fire. Using bellows, blowers, or other means of obtaining sufficient draft, the mold is raised to slightly above the melting point of the casting metal.

When using brass the Ashanti metalsmiths watch for the turquoise-colored flames that indicate that zinc is being vaporized from the molten brass. After heating the mold and crucible for a few minutes more to superheat the metal, the mold is removed from the fire and turned over so that the metal flows by gravity into the mold. The mold with the crucible on top is set aside until the metal solidifies and the mold is broken open. These steps are shown in the drawings in Figure 11.1. There are many more details required for successful casting, but the above description includes the major steps. The

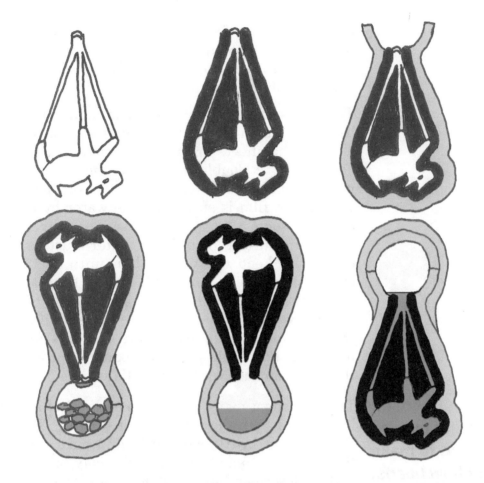

Figure 11.1 The steps in making an Ashanti lost-wax casting. Top row, left to right: the model and sprues, the model with layer of charcoal clay, adding outer clay to form mold. Bottom row, left to right: mold and unmelted metal, completed mold after melting metal, mold turned over and cooling.

method of constructing a furnace for Ashanti casting will be described at the end of this chapter.

Making the model

Wax models for Ashanti casting can be made of any wax available for model making. The materials and methods described in Chapter 3 are suitable; however, one of the features of Ashanti casting is the ability to cast hollow and very thin objects. Therefore, we will describe some of the special methods used by Ashanti craftsmen.

The traditional Ashanti model is made of natural beeswax, which is, in turn, made into wax wires or sheets. The sheets are made by melting chunks of beeswax in a double boiler and then pouring the molten wax carefully onto the surface of a pan of hot water. The film is spread on the water by blowing on it in such a way as to cause the wax to flow across the surface. The pan of water must be warm enough to keep the wax molten until the film is spread completely. Any bubbles that form are broken with a small probe. The wax and tray of water are allowed to cool so that the wax solidifies. The sheet of wax is cut lose where the wax and pan touch and the whole sheet of wax may be lifted from the water surface while it is still flexible.

Ashanti casting may be used to make hollow beads.

The wax sheet may be set aside to dry, but it is easier to work with the wax while it is warm. Beeswax is somewhat brittle when cold and hard. Pieces of the sheet wax may be formed over clay cores, which will be described later, and designs may be cut into or added to the wax sheet. If the wax sheet is too thick, it may be rolled thinner using a conventional rolling mill. The wax should be placed between pieces of paper to protect the rollers of the rolling mill.

Wax wire can be used to make designs. Wax wire is available from jeweler's suppliers in standard wire sizes with many different cross-sectional shapes. However, round wire can be made by cutting a strip of warm beeswax and rolling it between a board and a flat surface, as was done, and still is, by primitive societies.

Containers with relatively thin walls may be made by forming warm beeswax sheets over a core made of clay and charcoal. Larger diameter wax wires are used for sprues. Sometimes the sprues are designed to be part of the design while, at the same time, feeding metal into the finer or thinner parts of the mold.

Sprues cannot be too large or too numerous. Multiple sprues are used when necessary, and these are brought together to form a pouring cup, which will later join the crucible in which the metal is melted. In general, the methods for making models and spruing are similar to those described earlier in this text; however, special care is required to be certain that sprues and gates are of sufficient diameter and that the flowing metal can easily reach all parts of the mold. This is of concern with Ashanti casting, because the technique does not employ any external force except gravity to move the metal into the mold. Both centrifugal and vacuum casting apply additional forces to the metal that overcome the resistance of slightly undersized sprues and gates. From a practical standpoint, sprues can't be too numerous and they can't be too large. On the other hand, sprues can easily be undersized, and an imperfect casting will result.

When a model is to produce a hollow casting, a core is formed of a special clay-charcoal mixture that will be described later. It must be sturdy enough to withstand the casting forces, but it must also be somewhat fragile so that it can be broken up within the finished casting and removed.

The core is shaped as desired, taking care to support it on metal wire or pins, sometimes called *chaplets*, which will hold it in position after the wax model has melted. Sometimes cores are attached to the outer mold so that pins are not required.

Making a clay mold

Near the end of the 1500s, Benvenuto Cellini, one of the better-known early goldsmiths and sculptors, wrote his memoirs and included formulas for making clay molds for bronze casting. The usual practice for making clay molds, described by other early writers, was to mix clay with about 30 percent horse or cow dung. Cellini wrote that his own special formula included adding "cloth clippings" to the mixture. He then allowed the clay mixture to age for some time. Both dung and cloth fibers have the effect of increasing the strength of air-dried but unfired clay. This is called green strength. The rotted organic material may also alter the shrinkage of the clay while drying and will improve the permeability of the clay after burnout.

Swiss jeweler Max Frohlich developed clay formulas for making molds.

After much experimentation, Max Frohlich developed the formulas for the clay bodies required for making cores and molds for Ashanti casting. These formulas are designed to hold shrinkage to about one percent and provide a porous mold after being fired. The basic components are grog and Bentonite, which is a highly plastic clay. *Grog* is a ceramic material that has been heated to above 1000° C.

Essentially, three kinds of mold materials are required. First, a clay body containing charcoal is required for making cores. The resulting cores should have sufficient green strength to permit them to be handled while forming the wax model over the core. Second, after the wax model and sprue assembly has been constructed, a more fluid charcoal-clay body is required. This clay body is made by diluting the core material with additional water to about the consistency of heavy cream. Three layers of charcoal-clay (each about 1/8 inch thick) are painted on the model with a brush with a

Frohlich Clay Formulas

Charcoal Clay for Cores:

By volume:

> 1 cup fine ceramic grog (cone 10)
>
> 1 cup hardwood charcoal powder
>
> To the above components add
>
> 10% Bentonite clay by weight.

Mixing Instructions: Wear a dust mask. Mix the dry ingredients, and then wet the mixture with two or three tablespoons of denatured alcohol to break the surface tension. Then add distilled water and stir to produce a smooth mixture that will hold together when formed into a ball. (Don't add too much water at a time or it will become too fluid.) Let the mixture sleep (rest undisturbed) for 24 hours.

Charcoal Clay for Molds: To make a clay body suitable for the inner layers of a mold, add sufficient water to the above core formula to produce a mixture with the consistency of heavy cream.

Clay for Outer Molds:

> 7.5 lbs. coarse grog
>
> 2.5 lbs. fine grog
>
> 1 lb. Bentonite
>
> 2 cups chopped grass
>
> 500 ml. distilled water (approximate)

Other organic material such as chopped moss or sawdust can substitute for grass. Add sufficient water to the dry ingredients and mix until it has the consistency of cookie dough. Let sleep for 24 hours before use.

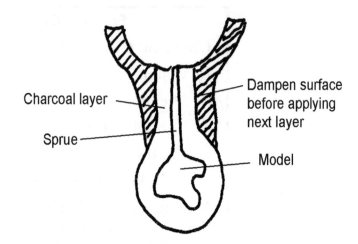

Charcoal layer

Sprue

Dampen surface
before applying
next layer

Model

**Figure 11.2
Partially finished flask
with the charcoal layer
and one layer of outer
clay completed.**

drying period between layers. Dab the clay onto the model rather than brushing and break any bubbles that form. When ready for the next coat, the charcoal-clay layer will turn gray and feel dry when held up and touched to your own face.

After at least three layers of charcoal-clay have been painted on a model, a thicker layer of outer-mold clay is added to strengthen the mold. This layer is about 1/8- to 1/4-inch thick and is added by massaging little balls of clay into shape over the model. Dampen the surface of the charcoal-clay so that the outer clay body will adhere. Care is required to avoid damaging the model and to get each blob of clay to adhere to the inner charcoal-clay layer and adjacent blobs of outer-mold clay. A partially finished mold is shown in Figure 11.2. After the first coat of outer-clay body is dry (it feels dry when touched to the cheek), a second coat is added in the same manner. This coat is flared to form a pouring cup around the sprue. Additional coats may be added if more strength is necessary. When the last coat is air dry, the mold may be placed sprue down next to a fire or some hot charcoal to melt the wax model. This process also hardens the mold

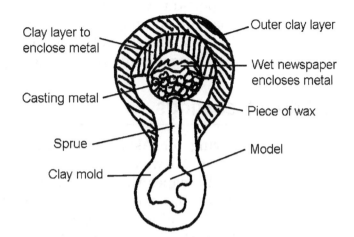

Clay layer to enclose metal

Casting metal

Sprue

Clay mold

Outer clay layer

Wet newspaper encloses metal

Piece of wax

Model

**Figure 11.3
Flask after crucible, metal, and outer clay coating has been applied.**

somewhat and makes it a little less fragile during subsequent steps.

It is not absolutely necessary to melt the wax out of the mold at this stage. Some craftsmen in Cameroon simply allow the wax to diffuse out through the walls of the mold during the final burnout of the mold. Sometimes the initial burnout is used to collect the wax so that it can be reused.

After the molds are cool enough to handle, a plug of wax is placed over the sprue hole and the required amount of unmelted metal is then added to the pouring cup. The pouring cup will become part of a crucible in which the metal will be melted. What will become the bottom of the crucible is formed by placing a dome of clay over the pile of metal in the pouring cup. It is useful to wrap the metal in a moistened piece of paper to prevent scraps of clay from mixing with the pieces of metal. Figure 11.3 shows the finished mold after the pouring cup and bundle of metal has been covered with clay.

A crude crucible, made using raku pottery techniques, can be used to contain the metal. This is important when casting with gold or silver. A final coat of clay may be placed over the entire mold to increase the strength before firing. At this point the mold is generally referred to as a flask.

Firing Ashanti castings

Firing for Ashanti casting has several purposes. First, all wax remaining in the mold is vaporized and escapes through the porous walls of the mold. Next, the clay gains strength that will withstand the handling that occurs when the mold is removed from the furnace. Finally, the firing will melt the metal that is encased in the flask. Frohlich developed a small firing and melting furnace constructed by lining a 10-gallon trash can with fire bricks (details described later). This is large enough to fire a number of small objects or a small sculpture. Firing is commenced by preheating the furnace with a small fire to which is added a layer of hardwood charcoal chunks. Hardwood charcoal is preferred to charcoal briquettes because less ash is formed. Several flasks are then placed on the bed of charcoal with the crucible containing the metal on the bottom. It is important for the metal to melt, but not run into the mold until the mold is removed from the furnace and turned over.

After the flasks are arranged on the bottom layer of charcoal, additional smaller chunks (thumb-sized) are packed around the flasks until the tops of the flasks just show. Preheat for ten minutes and then remove the flasks and fill the furnace three-fourths full of charcoal. Replace the flasks on the new layer of charcoal and pack additional charcoal around the flasks. When fully packed, the top of the flasks will be just visible at the top of the furnace, surrounded by charcoal.

One should wear a respirator for most of the firing for protection from toxic fumes that will issue from some molten alloys.

For the first fifteen minutes allow the fire to gradually get hotter and strengthen the molds. When the charcoal at the bottom becomes bright red the new charcoal at the top of the furnace will ignite with a "whoosh." An almost smokeless flame will continue at the top. The flasks should become a tawny brown color before a hair-dryer blower is turned on.

The blower should be placed in the hole near the bottom of the furnace and turned on for 15 minutes, then stop and add more charcoal chunks around the flasks. Tamp carefully. Then turn the blower on for another 15-minute cycle. Finally, the flames will change to a turquoise blue, and the coals at the top of the furnace will get a yellow coating from the zinc fumes when you are casting brass. (If other alloys such as gold or silver are to be cast, some craftsmen will add a flask containing brass to the furnace in order to use the above indicators that the metal has melted.) Turn off the blower and add more charcoal to keep flasks covered. Wait five minutes with the blower off and then turn on the blower for a final five minutes to superheat the molten metal.

The appearance of the turquoise flame and white smoke signals that the brass has melted. After the final five-minute cycle with the blower turned on, turn the blower off and quickly unpack the flasks. Remove any charcoal that obstructs the tongs that will be used to remove the flasks.

Finally, using leather welder's gloves and long-handled tongs, grasp the flasks one at a time and quickly turn each one over before removing it from the furnace. This allows the metal to flow by gravity into the mold cavity. Set each flask on firebricks supported so that the crucible is now at the top of the flask and the molten metal remains in the mold. The flask will still be glowing red at first. When it turns gray, sprinkle water on the mold and break off the crucible end of the flask by tapping it with a hammer. A nicely formed metal "button" should fill the sprue opening. If the metal is not all melted or if the mold appears to not be completely filled, it is possible to re-invest the mold and repeat the burn-out. The mold will probably be strong enough to withstand any repeated handling.

When the flask has cooled sufficiently, break the flask and remove the cast object and the still-attached sprue and button. Finally, cut off the sprues and finish the object using files, sandpaper, and any of the usual jewelry-finishing techniques.

Constructing a furnace

The Frohlich furnace is constructed using a 10-gallon galvanized trash can as an outer container. The first step is to cut a 2-1/2-inch diameter hole in the side of the trash can about two inches from the bottom.

Supplies for Furnace Construction

10 gallon galvanized trash can

40 lb. bag Mizzou® castable refractory

5 lb. can SairBond® refractory mortar

1/2 yard of Fiberfax® blanket

8 ea. Clipper split firebricks

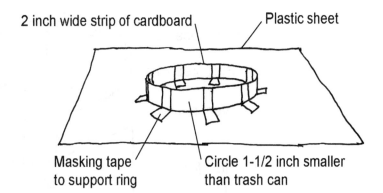

2 inch wide strip of cardboard   Plastic sheet

Figure 11.4
Form to cast false
bottom for furnace.

Masking tape
to support ring

Circle 1-1/2 inch smaller
than trash can

Next a false bottom is constructed using Mizzou castable refractory cement. The false bottom is made by setting up a two-inch-wide strip of corrugated box material as shown in Figure 11.4. The inside diameter of the mold should be about 1-1/2 inches less than the inside diameter of the bottom of the trash can. Line the cardboard mold with a plastic bag to make it waterproof and fill it with the castable cement that has been combined with water to make a stiff mixture. Poke eight or nine holes all the way through the cement with a finger and insert half-inch dowels covered with plastic (or try pieces of PVC tubing) to keep the holes open. Allow the false bottom to harden over night.

The remainder of the mixed batch of castable cement should be used to cover the bottom of the trash can with a one-inch refractory layer. Several 1/4-brick-size pieces of firebrick should be embedded in the cement to support the false bottom, which will be set on top of the bricks. After the refractory cement has hardened overnight, place the false bottom on top of the bricks.

Then take a piece of Fiberfax® insulating sheet and line the wall of the trash can. This can be pushed down in the space between the false bottom and the

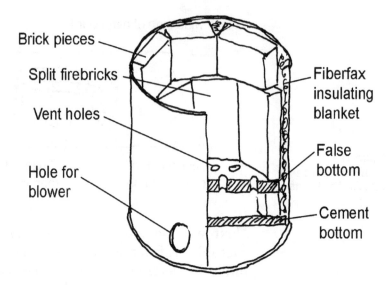

Brick pieces

Split firebricks

Vent holes

Hole for blower

Fiberfax insulating blanket

False bottom

Cement bottom

**Figure 11.5
Cut away section of
Frohlich furnace
design.**

wall of the trash can. Moisten and place half-fire-bricks and pieces of firebricks around the circumference of the furnace as shown in Figure 11.5.

Cement all the bricks in place with refractory kiln mortar and seal the top (where the insulating mat shows) with additional castable cement. The finished furnace is shown in the photograph, Figure 11.6.

After the refractory cement has hardened, cure the furnace by building a charcoal fire inside it with a paper starter. Set the trash can lid on the can, partially open to create a draft.

Locating refractory materials for the furnace

Refractory materials are not usually available at your local hardware store. A good way to find fire-brick and refractory mortar is to do an Internet search for "refractory material" or "kiln refractory supplies."

**Figure 11.6
Photograph of
completed Frohlich
furnace.**

Step-by-step Ashanti casting

1. Obtain a commercial wax model or make a wax model using standard techniques.

2. Sprue model appropriately. Larger diameter and longer sprues may be desirable for gravity casting to generate sufficient pouring force.

3. Weigh the model and sprue assembly. Record the weight:_____

4. Coat the surface of the model with a wetting agent.

5. Paint on a layer of charcoal-clay.

6. Allow to air dry.

7. Repeat for three coats.

8. Add a coat of Frohlich outer-mold clay. Then let it dry.

9. Add another coat of outer-mold clay and form a pouring cup. Let dry.

10. After the clay has dried, set mold near a fire or glowing charcoal with sprue down so that the wax will melt out.

11. When cool enough to handle, plug sprue hole with a piece of wax and place pre-weighed metal in pouring cup. (It may be easier to wrap the metal in a piece of paper before going to the next step.)

12. When using gold or silver, place a small raku crucible over the metal. (This keeps mold clay from mixing with the metal.) Then enclose the metal, paper, crucible, and all with outer-mold clay. Let dry.

13. Add extra coats of outer-mold clay as necessary to strengthen the mold.

14. When dry, the mold is ready for burnout. It may be called a flask at this point.

15. Break hardwood charcoal into walnut-sized pieces and use paper to get a bed of coals started in furnace.

16. Fill the furnace one-fourth full of charcoal and place the flasks on the charcoal in the furnace with the crucible and pouring cup downward. Pack additional charcoal around flasks until the tops just show.

17. Pre-heat flasks for ten minutes while the charcoal begins to catch fire. Don't use a blower at this point. Bring temperature up slowly so that the mold becomes harder and stronger.

18. Remove the flasks with a gloved hand and fill the furnace three-quarters full of charcoal. Replace flasks on top of charcoal and carefully pack charcoal around the flasks. The tops should just show.

19. Allow fire to get hotter gradually without using a blower.

20. After the fire is bright at the bottom the remaining charcoal will ignite with a "whoosh." An almost smokeless flame will continue at the top of the furnace.

21. Tamp the charcoal gently and turn on the hairdryer blower for 15 minutes.

22. Use a respirator while working from now on because toxic fumes will be given off when some alloys start to melt.

23. Turn off blower, tamp, and add charcoal. Then turn on blower again.

24. If flasks containing brass are in the furnace, the coals will get a yellow coating and the fire changes to a turquoise color when the zinc in the brass starts to vaporize. Blue-white smoke will appear. Let heat for five minutes with the blower off.

25. Turn on blower for a final five minutes.

26. Turn off blower and unpack flasks by removing pieces of charcoal from between the flasks with long-handled tongs.

27. Using the tongs, lift flasks from the furnace, one at a time, and immediately invert so that the metal flows into the mold. (The flasks can be inverted while the flasks are still resting on the bed of coals before lifting them from the furnace.)

28. Set aside on firebricks to cool with the mold down. (Don't allow the flask to tip over as this will permit the still-molten metal to run out of the sprue. The flasks are still red-hot and the metal will remain molten for some time.)

29. When the flasks become gray instead of red, sprinkle water on them to cool them further and break off the crucible end of the flask to observe the button of metal still left in the pouring cup. (If most of the metal has entered the mold and a

small button shows, the cast is probably successful.)

30. If the metal is not all melted it is possible to cool
    the flask, re-invest and repeat the burnout.

31. When cool, break the flask and remove the
    object. Clean off any clay adhering to the metal.

32. Clean and polish using standard jewelry finish-
    ing methods.

Cleanup and Finishing

Overview

Lost-wax castings may be finished using hand methods, power-assisted tools, and/or what are called mass-finishing methods. Traditional hand methods involve the use of files, sandpaper, and a polishing cloth charged with rouge. No power tools are involved, yet it is possible to produce a perfect finish. In fact, high-precision optical finishing involves handwork.

Power-assisted tools do not produce a better finish. They simply improve the efficiency and can, in fact, result in inferior results if not used properly. Finally, mass-finishing methods involve the use of vibrating tumblers with various cutting and polishing media to eliminate most handwork.

Cleanup

Cleanup begins shortly after the cast and before the flask has cooled to room temperature. Using a pair of tongs, remove the flask from whatever casting equipment has been used and place it on a firebrick or other fireproof surface. Wait until the red glow ceases to be evident from the button in the sprue cup. It may be necessary to dim or turn off the lights to determine when the sprue button is gray instead of hot. When the color leaves the sprue button, the flask is still quite hot so take it with a pair of tongs and slowly lower the flask below the surface of a bucket of water as shown in Figure 12.1. It will bubble and foam and the investment will start to disintegrate. Lower it all the way into the water and

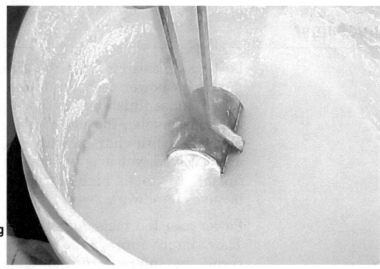

Figure 12.1
Breaking up investment by placing flask in bucket of water.

after all the foaming and bubbling has stopped you may reach into the water to find the casting. It may have fallen out of the flask or it may be embedded in some investment still in the flask. If still in the flask use a spatula or old spoon to push the rest of the investment out of the flask. Locate and carefully test the temperature of the casting, which should be cool enough to touch after a few minutes in the water. Larger masses cool more slowly and could be hot enough to burn if one is in too much of a rush.

Investment may be chemically removed. Remove any investment clinging to the casting with an old toothbrush. Some investment may be trapped in crevices and will require some probing, but be careful not to scratch the casting with a sharp tool. Diluted hydrochloric acid (also called muriatic acid) or one of several commercially available divesting solutions may be used to aid in removing the remaining investment. At this point the casting will be annealed and clean and ready for final finishing.

The first finishing step is to remove the sprues, which should be saved to mix with new metal for later castings. Sometimes sprues are cut off with a bolt cutter; however, this usually leaves a significant unwanted spur of metal that must be filed off. If the casting is gold, it is generally desirable to minimize the amount of gold wasted. Under these circumstances, a jeweler's saw is the preferable method for removing sprues as close to the casting as possible. One must be careful, however, to avoid cutting too close and removing part of the actual casting. It is easier to carefully remove metal than to replace metal when too much is removed. Use a single-cut mill file to remove the major mass of the metal and then use a rubber pumice wheel on a polishing machine or a flexible-shaft tool to dress the remaining evidence of the sprue or sprues.

Hand finishing

A number of years ago, as part of an initiation process, I was required to take a small section of iron rail that was roughly cut and shape it to symmetrical measurements and then sand and polish it to a mirror finish without the use of any power tools. Files, emery paper, and crocus cloth charged with rouge are really precision tools. A fine finish may be obtained with only these three tools, although most persons are not willing to take the time and care that is required.

A large machinist's file can be used to remove sprues.

Hand finishing implies the use of hand tools, although the use of a flex-shaft tool and buffer is considered by some persons to be hand finishing. Files, emery paper, and buffers all have a place in hand finishing. Files are used to shape or remove masses of metal before progressive grades of emery paper are used to smooth surfaces. A large 10-inch machinist's single-cut file will remove the remains of a sprue in a few strokes and will leave a relatively smooth finish. Always start with the largest and coarsest file and then use progressively finer files until all evidence of the sprue attachment is eliminated. Be careful not to overuse the large coarse file or the object may start to disappear. This is not to suggest that a finer file should be used instead; merely use the coarse file with care.

Files are used to completely shape the object. Single-cut files are available in several shapes such as round, half round, triangular, or flat to match a surface that requires shaping. Except for fine jeweler's files, I prefer to work with single-cut machinist's files rather than double-cut files that are designed to aggressively remove metal. Note that the double-cut files have a number of small pointed teeth that leave scratches that must be removed by extra work with successively finer files. On the other hand, a new single-cut file shears off layers of metal leaving minor scratches to be removed. Most jewelers' files are double cut, so I prefer to use only the finest jeweler's files before using sandpaper.

After the casting is appropriately shaped, sanding sticks with successively finer grades of grit may be used to smooth the object. I find that 200- and 600-grit emery papers work well. Sanding sticks or emery paper glued to tongue depressors are useful for this purpose. Examples are shown in Figure 12.2. String coated with grit is available for finishing surfaces inside a penetrating hole.

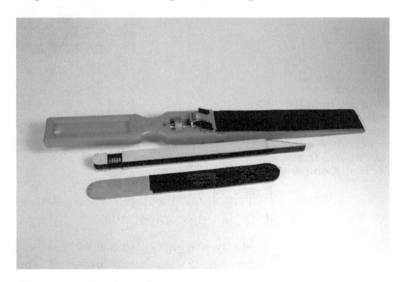

Figure 12.2
An assortment of sanding sticks for finishing jewelry castings.

Fine scratch removal and pre-polish are achieved using a buffing wheel charged with Tripoli, a dark brown buffing compound. A Tripoli buff will remove some metal but it should not be expected to remove deep scratches. After carefully washing the casting with soap and water, the final polish is created using a separate buffing wheel charged with rouge. The final polish using a buffing wheel charged with rouge or some other final polish compound should require only a few seconds if all previous smoothing steps have been carried out properly. Everyone has his or her favorite substitute or replacement for

**Figure 12.3
Vibrating tumbler
used for mass
finishing small pieces
of jewelry (Photo
courtesy of The
Contenti Company)**

Tripoli and rouge, which are ancient buffing and polishing compounds.

Many jewelers use a motor-driven flexible-shaft tool for hand finishing jewelry. The flex-shaft tool is merely a mechanization of the hand tools just described. Rotary files, sandpaper disks, and small pumice wheels replace the hand tools described above. Small buffs charged with Tripoli or rouge are used for the final finishing and polishing steps. A particularly useful wheel for use with a flex-shaft tool is the knife-edge silicone wheel. These wheels incorporate a fine grit for removing metal but will leave the surface with a relatively high polish. They are particularly useful for touch-up or for correcting small errors. The coarsest rubber wheels remove metal almost as fast as a file although considerably more heat is generated. The finest silicone wheels

**Figure 12.4
A barrel tumbler that
may be used for
finishing small
castings.**

cut very slowly and produce a finish that is practically a final polish.

Mass finishing

If care has been used in making the original wax
model, very little filing is required to finish shaping
the object. Most of the time a file is used to remove
the metal projection where the sprue was attached,
and then the castings can be processed using mass-
finishing techniques with no additional handwork.
Mass finishing methods employ vibrating finishers
similar to the one shown in Figure 12.3. Coarse,
medium, and fine grit plastic cutting media are
used for several hours each to "cut down" and
"deburr" castings. Flow-through systems use water
to remove fine debris that is produced. In a six-step
process, non-abrasive micro-polish porcelain balls,
clean walnut shell, and finally rouge-charged walnut shell follow the cutting media. Barrel tumblers

similar to the one shown in Figure 12.4 also may be used to produce similar results. The objective is to eliminate all hand work except the initial sprue removal. If high-quality models are used, it may be possible to eliminate the coarse cutting media and perhaps abbreviate some of the other steps. In addition, frequent cleaning to remove cutting debris and recharging is necessary.

Some craftsmen combine hand methods and mass-finishing methods by doing additional hand filing before placing articles in a vibrating tumbler containing steel shot to tumble polish for an hour or two. Tumbling with steel shot leaves a polished finish surface that is slightly hardened by the peening effect of the tumbling shot. This is sometimes called *shot peening.* Also, if the wax model was free of scratches and pits, a high polish may be achieved on the casting by touching up the tumble finish with a rouge wheel or by placing the casting in a vibratory tumbler containing walnut shells and rouge. The more care used in making the wax model, the less finishing is required on the casting.

13

Casting
Problems

Overview

Casting defects are the results of improper casting procedures. We have tried to identify the reasons for most casting procedures elsewhere in this book. While it is possible to go back and read each chapter when defects occur, this chapter is designed to help quickly find the cause of various problems so that they can be corrected. The discussion here should be used with the Troubleshooting Table in the Appendix.

Porosity

Porosity is a casting problem that may result from many possible causes that fall into two general categories. Porosity has the appearance of a lot of small pits in the surface of the casting. Frequently, porosity does not become apparent until the final finishing stages of a piece of jewelry. Some forms of porosity may occur deep within the casting and will not become apparent during final finishing. It is not uncommon for more than one kind of porosity to occur in a single casting.

Gas porosity

Gas porosity is not as common as some of the other forms of porosity. It results from gas becoming trapped within the metal while the metal is melted. Gas porosity can be recognized as small, irregularly shaped bubbles that appear on the surface of a casting. The gases most likely to be absorbed by molten metal are oxygen and hydrogen that are present in the atmosphere. The best way to keep them from reacting with the molten metal is to protect the molten pool of metal from contact with the atmosphere. A method used in some professional casting systems is to carry out the entire casting process in a vacuum or by covering the metal with an inert gas such as argon while it is in the molten state. Covering the pool of molten metal with a layer of boric acid flux is also effective if the metal is melted in an open crucible.

Using a graphite crucible will protect the molten metal with a covering of inert carbon dioxide that is formed by oxygen reacting with the carbon in the crucible. Graphite crucibles or liners are used in some electrically heated melting pots and in the electrically heated melting furnace on the arms of some casting machines. Open clay-graphite crucibles are also manufactured to produce the same effect. Borax fluxes are not used with graphite crucibles.

A common way that oxygen is introduced while torch melting is by holding the torch too close to the metal so that the metal is exposed to the oxygen-rich inner cone of burning gas. This is the pale blue cone of flame nearest to the torch tip. Metal should always be melted in the reducing atmosphere just beyond the blue inner cone. Molten metal does not absorb the fuel gas as readily as it absorbs oxygen.

Finally, it is possible to obtain deoxidized casting grain, which contains a material that will become chemically attached to any oxygen that is present. Both gold and silver deoxidized casting alloys are available from precious metal suppliers. In practice, more than one of the above protective measures may be taken.

Shrinkage porosity

Shrinkage porosity results from poor model design and/or poor sprueing practice. Porosity of this type results when a cooling casting shrinks and additional molten metal is not allowed to flow into the shrinking volume. This results in a casting that does not fill the original void of the mold, and little pinpoint pits or gray areas appear on the casting surface. As the casting is finished the pinpoint voids may grow into a larger bubble or wormlike holes that penetrate the casting and become larger with further polishing. Some voids due to shrinkage porosity may be completely contained within the casting.

In an earlier chapter the progressive cooling of a cast object was discussed. To prevent shrinkage porosity, the design of the object as well as the sprues must be configured so that the model solidifies first, followed by the sprues and any risers. The design of the object itself must permit progressive cooling within the casting, and the sprues and any risers should be attached to the last part of the model to solidify. Any departure from the above cooling sequence will result in shrinkage porosity. This is because the last part of the object to solidify will not be able to draw molten metal from another segment and will become porous as it shrinks so that it no longer completely fills the mold void. If the entire system has been correctly designed the only shrinkage will appear on the top of the button in the pouring cup.

Let us consider the model first: If there are heavy masses as well as thin or light sections, sprues must be attached to the heavy mass or masses. A riser is used to supply metal to a cooling segment of the casting that may not be conveniently attached to a sprue leading to the pouring cup. The riser is also cut off because it is not part of the model and any shrinkage porosity on the riser does not affect the casting.

Models that are too close together may develop shrinkage porosity. It is possible for even a properly designed model to experience shrinkage porosity if models are placed too close together on a casting tree. Masses on adjacent models may supply sufficient heat to prevent proper cooling of a properly designed model. For example, if several models are clustered together to form a significant thermal mass, the sprues could "freeze" or solidify before the castings and result in shrinkage porosity. This type of shrinkage porosity can be identified by noting that models in a certain part of the casting tree contain porosity.

A final type of shrinkage porosity occurs when the flask is too hot when metal is injected. Models in a flask that is too hot will freeze more slowly than in a cooler flask. The longer cooling time permits greater shrinkage in the more massive model elements and, at least theoretically, will result in porosity in a model that otherwise would cast perfectly. Because it is not possible to know the exact temperature in every part of a flask that is cooling in free air, most casting protocols recommend that the burnout oven temperature be reduced to a proper casting temperature at least an hour before casting. In addition to preventing cooling porosity, it is desirable for the model to cool rapidly for metallurgical reasons. This effect will be discussed below under the heading "Casting Temperature."

Hot tears

Hot tears are related to shrinkage porosity, but occur due to an entirely different phenomenon. A hot tear can occur in an otherwise satisfactory model when part of the model is constrained in such a way that cooling causes a segment of the model to develop internal stresses during the cooling process. According to Romanoff this occurs when "an abrupt change; for example, going from a heavy section of the casting to a thin section of the casting [occurs] while making a sharp bend." He recommends that such design elements be avoided or an extra sprue may be added to solve the problem. He also notes that a hot tear can sometimes be avoided by simply changing the casting alloy, because some alloys have greater shrinkage than others.

Brittleness

A casting may appear to be brittle when it is quenched while too hot. Rather than brittleness, the casting may actually fracture or develop small cracks that will then suddenly give way under stress, giving the impression that the casting is brittle.

Foreign particles

The presence of foreign particles in a mold can cause imperfections that at first glance may appear to be porosity. Several potential sources of foreign particles exist. Melting metal in a crucible that has been improperly fluxed can result in particles being flaked off and included in the metal entering the mold. Attaching a sprue with a sharp transition between the sprue and model may permit small pieces of investment to be broken off and embedded in the casting. Mixing investment with too much water aggravates this sort of defect. Investment prepared with too much water will have significantly reduced mold strength.

Foreign particles in a casting may also result from models that do not burn out completely. This occurs most frequently when a non-wax model, such as a bug, is cast directly. While most organic objects (anything that is or was living) will burn out completely, some bugs such as cockroaches contain inorganic substances that will not vaporize at normal burnout temperatures. Otherwise, organic objects such as pinecones, flowers, bugs, etc., make good lost-wax casting models.

Foreign particles that result in an imperfect model also might become trapped in the wax. For example, a file used for filing metal might transfer metal shavings to a wax model being prepared with the same file. It is therefore best to keep metal and wax files separate, although I have often used opposite sides of the same machinist's file to remove wax on a model and then to remove the metal stub of a sprue.

Incomplete castings

Incomplete castings can result from several causes. The most obvious is too low a temperature of the molten metal used for the casting, allowing the metal to freeze in the sprue system before the cavity has completely filled. If the molten metal is cooler than 75° F above the melting point of the alloy, it is likely that an incomplete casting will result. Between 75° and 150° above the alloy melting point, a ring, for example, may fill completely, but the two streams of metal flowing around the two sides of the shank will not fuse completely. This has been called "cold porosity." To avoid cold porosity, Romanoff recommends that the casting alloy should be heated to 170° to 180° F above the alloy melting temperature.

It should be obvious that the mold temperature also affects the speed with which the metal solidifies: the hotter the mold the slower the speed of solidification.

Incorrect casting temperatures

A mold at too high a temperature can also cause problems, however. Several recommendations exist regarding metal and mold casting temperatures, but textbooks on casting seldom present the complete rationale. If models are designed correctly, sprues are properly attached, and a mold is correctly prepared, there are still other variables to consider. What should be the casting temperature of the mold and what should be the temperature of the casting metal?

If one is melting casting grain with a torch, little can be done to determine the exact temperature of the metal. The usual recommendation is to continue to heat the grain with a reducing flame until a fluid and shiny puddle is produced in the crucible. Descriptions of the metal surface "swirling" or "rolling" are sometimes offered, but these provide no information about the metal temperature. On the other hand, there are usually specific recommendations about the flask temperature. Further investigation reveals that the flask and metal temperature interact, and recommendations from precious metal dealers generally recommend specific flask and metal temperatures for each alloy. The situation is not simple, and various temperature modifications are often required when commercially casting large trees and flasks.

Rapid flask cooling produces a fine-grained casting. Mold and metal temperatures interact because both affect the rate at which metal freezes, or solidifies, in the mold. In general, it is desirable for the metal to freeze rapidly to produce a fine-grained casting. Metal has a crystalline structure and small crystal size is related to desirable mechanical properties of the finished casting. On the other hand, alloys of precious metals become fluid over a range of temperatures. The metal initially forms a sludge-like semi-fluid mass and finally becomes completely molten and fluid as the temperature is raised.

Each alloy has specific characteristics and the recommendations of the metal supplier should be followed for precision casting. Additives such as boron and silicon, which are used to produce deoxidized alloys, raise the necessary casting temperature. An additive, such as zinc, lowers the melting point of an alloy. Hundreds of different alloy combinations may be available from a single metal manufacturer, so it is difficult to generalize regarding temperature. Trial and error is often required. This is especially significant if scrap metal of unknown composition is used. Metal suppliers generally recommend a 50:50

mixture of new and used casting grain to maintain normal casting characteristics of a specific alloy.

Cast with metal 150° to 200° F above the alloy melting point.

While highly specific recommendations depend on the alloy in use, most texts recommend a metal temperature that is 150° to 200° F above the melting point of the alloy. The flask should be at a temperature that is somewhere between 800° and 1000° F depending on the fineness of the model detail. Not a very precise instruction, is it? On the other hand, instructions that accompany one deoxidized 14 K gold alloy recommend raising the flask casting temperature to as much as 1350° F, which is the highest burnout temperature recommended for gypsum investment. In other words, casting is done without reducing the flask temperature as is normally recommended in published burnout profiles.

I have found it satisfactory to remove a 2 x 2-1/2-inch flask from a 1350° oven and cast within a minute or two using a deoxidized silver alloy. With torch melting, I cast when the metal becomes molten and shiny to avoid overheating. When casting using a melting pot or a furnace that is part of the casting machine, the metal should be cast at 1800° to 1900° F. This method has worked satisfactorily in a classroom environment; however, experienced volume casters warn that the casting may be rougher than desirable using this approach.

The general recommendation is to select the appropriate casting temperature for the metal and vary the flask temperature to solve various temperature-related problems. The flask temperature should be kept as low as possible to cause rapid solidification and a resulting fine-grained metal. Massive objects may be cast at a lower flask temperature than small objects with fine detail.

Insufficient permeability

Quality investment casting in the jewelry industry depends on adequate permeability of the investment so that trapped gases can be expelled from the mold during the actual casting process. This is particularly important in vacuum-assisted casting because one is limited to the atmospheric pressure of about 15 pounds per square inch to push metal into the sprues and mold. Centrifugal casting machines are much more "forgiving" because the metal can be injected with greater force simply by winding the spring an extra turn or two to increase the acceleration rate.

Inadequate burnout causes poor investment permeability.

Under any circumstance the permeability of the investment must be as high as possible. A good burnout is the first requirement, as emphasized in the chapter on burnout. Too short a burnout schedule or too many flasks in an oven for a specific burnout cycle can result in inadequate burnout. The consequence of inadequate burnout is inevitably poor investment permeability.

Proper burnout can still result in insufficient permeability if the flask is large and/or contains many models. If the position of a model is such that the gases must pass through a long tortuous pathway while being drawn through the investment, the mold may not fill completely. There are several solutions to this problem. The most obvious one is to apply more force to the metal, and this is the reason that centrifugal casting is more forgiving. Other approaches are required for vacuum-assisted casting.

Perforated flasks minimize investment resistance to gas flow.

Perforated flasks evolved from the need to reduce the resistance to gas flow during vacuum-assisted casting. This was explained in the chapter on vacuum casting, but it is reemphasized here because this is one of the solutions to a problem of inadequate mold filling. Usually one uses a vacuum-assisted casting machine specifically arranged for use with flanged perforated flasks that project down inside a vacuum chamber. As an alternative, a flat-top vacuum table can be used with a large perforated flask if some sort of vacuum chamber is devised that will contain the perforated flask and seal around the flange.

Oxidation of the casting

While a casting is cooling after injecting the casting metal, air, which contains oxygen, will penetrate the investment and react with the hot metal to create a black oxide on the surface of the casting. This is an additional coating that must be removed during the finishing process, and anything that will eliminate the oxide will simplify finishing.

Some commercial casting systems are designed to function in a complete vacuum or in an atmosphere of a neutral gas oxide formation is completely eliminated by preventing oxygen from contacting the casting during cooling.

An ad hoc solution developed by a caster in California is to remove oxygen from the atmosphere surrounding the cooling flask. This is achieved by taking the hot flask from the casting machine and placing it in a chamber with some flammable material that will use up the oxygen in the chamber. This approach was described in an article in *Rock and Gem*. Closing up the hot flask in a chamber with some scrap wax produces smoke and effectively consumes the oxygen in the chamber. The result is a clean, smooth, non-oxidized casting.

Deoxidized casting grain eliminates the black oxide coating.

A final solution to oxidation is to use so-called "deoxidized" casting grain. These alloys contain small amounts of boron and/or silicon that "scavenge" any oxygen that penetrates the investment and produces clean castings without any other special precautions. Deoxidized casting grain is more expensive than conventional casting grain; however, the additional cost is probably minimal for a small-volume caster. The extra cost may be a different economic consideration in a volume production shop.

Troubleshooting

The long discussion in this chapter is directed toward developing an understanding of the causes of various casting defects. Rules of thumb may be helpful in some cases. For example, one casting expert said, "Seventy percent of all porosity problems can be traced to poor burnout." A table of defects, causes, and potential remedies, however, may aid in troubleshooting a particular problem. Appendix E is a Troubleshooting Table developed from several sources. Much of it is based on material posted on the Internet site of United Precious Metal Refining, Inc., Alden, NY. (www.unitedpmr.com)

14

Metals and Alloys for Casting

Overview

Many metals and alloys may be cast using lost-wax techniques. At some time at least six thousand years ago, attempts were made to cast copper. A few copper castings have been found. However, we often hear of the Bronze Age as ushering in the use of metal for tools and arms. Why not the Copper Age? The reason is that bronze is much easier to cast than pure copper.

True bronze is an alloy of copper and tin that was widely used during the Bronze Age and is still in use today. Alloys used during the Bronze Age vary significantly in composition and are often composed of metals other than copper and tin. It is clear that considerable experimentation led to the modern, more or less standard, bronze composition of 96 percent copper and 4 percent tin.

The manufacture of metal objects by casting was not feasible until it was discovered that a mixture of copper and another metal or metals—called an alloy—could be poured into molds to reproduce objects that had previously been made from stone or perhaps from natural metallic copper or gold.

Some of the oldest known objects cast by the lost-wax process are called bronze and were found hidden in a cave near the Dead Sea in Israel: the Nahal Mishmar hoard. The objects were cast around 4000 BCE from what is actually a bronze-looking alloy composed of copper, arsenic, and antimony. This alloy is not used today, and most of the ancient bronze objects are made of a copper-tin alloy similar to modern-day bronze. However, recent experiments by metallurgists at Oxford University have reproduced the alloy and determined that it has very good casting properties and is, in fact, an excellent alloy for lost-wax casting.

Jeweler's bronze is actually brass. A second common yellowish alloy is brass, which is composed of copper and zinc. Brass evolved much later than bronze because the smelting of zinc requires more sophisticated techniques than either copper or tin. In fact, early copper-tin alloys were probably made by smelting a mixture of ores rather than by producing pure metals that were later mixed together to produce the bronze alloy. One alloy, called jeweler's bronze, is actually a brass composed of 88 percent copper and 12 percent zinc. Brass is also made with a variety of compositions. For example, increasing the copper fraction to 90 percent produces so-called red brass.

Another non-precious metal alloy is pewter, which originally was composed of lead and tin. The origin of this silver-looking alloy is also lost in history, but its development is a natural step in the evolution of casting alloys, because lead is an easy metal to smelt at relatively low temperatures. Old pewter was often used for cooking and eating utensils and was the poor-man's substitute for silver, which served a similar use among the wealthy. The old pewter alloy melts at a much lower temperature than silver, brass, or bronze and, therefore, is much easier to cast or work. Modern pewter does not contain lead for health reasons. The current pewter alloy is composed of 91 percent tin, 7 percent antimony, and 2 percent copper. Sometimes the name Britannia metal is used interchangeably with pewter when referring to the modern alloy.

Modern pewter does not contain lead.

Finally, aluminum should be mentioned as a non-precious metal suitable for lost-wax casting. Although not a common metal for jewelry casting, aluminum melts at 1220 degrees Fahrenheit, which is somewhat lower than bronze, the brasses, or precious metals such as gold, silver, or platinum. Pure aluminum is not difficult to cast, but it is soft and might only be useful for display models or very massive pieces of jewelry. Probably other non-precious white metals such as nickel silver are more suitable for most cast jewelry. Nickel silver (also called German silver or white brass) contains no silver and is composed of about 60 percent copper, 20 percent zinc, and 20 percent nickel. It should be noted that some persons are allergic to nickel.

The precious metals—primarily gold, silver, and platinum—are excellent for lost-wax casting. Pure or almost pure gold and silver may be found in nature. Some early metal objects were formed by pounding pure gold into shape; however, both gold and silver are rather soft in the pure form, and most castings are made from alloys that are both harder and melt at a lower temperature. Ancient artifacts have been found composed of a naturally occurring alloy of gold and silver called *electrum*.

Gold

Gold is, by far, the most popular of precious metals for jewelry manufacture. It is available in sufficient quantity, but is scarce enough to be valuable. Its resistance to tarnishing makes it very desirable for jewelry making. Alloys composed of gold and different amounts of copper and other metals have properties suitable for both metal fabrication and casting.

24 K gold is 999.9/1000 fine.

The fineness of gold is represented by the term karat which is usually abbreviated K or k. Twenty-four karat gold is 999.9 fine or essentially pure gold. Often one will see a gold article referred to as 14 KY or 14 KW indicating that it is either yellow or white 14 K gold.

Alloys such as 22 K, 18 K, 14 K, etc., contain respectively 22, 18, and 14 parts gold out of a total of 24 parts. Thus 18 K gold is 18/24 or 75 percent gold. Ten K gold, the least fine gold in common use for jewelry, is 10/24 or 42 percent gold. The balance of the yellow gold alloys is composed primarily of silver, copper, and zinc. White gold is alloyed with palladium, a relatively less common member of the platinum family of metals. Table 14.1 lists a number of the common alloys of gold. The particular alloy composition chosen is somewhat a matter of taste, however. Alloys with as little as 42 percent gold may be used for fine jewelry, but available alloys with lower fractions of gold are not considered karat gold.

Pure gold, or 24-karat gold, is soft and very malleable. Gold leaf production is the primary use for 24 K gold. The extreme malleability makes it possible to hammer the gold into very thin sheets that are used to coat objects made of other baser materials. It was found in ancient times that pure gold would not work-harden when pounded into thin sheets while all alloys of gold will harden and will tear or break when hammered into thin sheets. Of course, the gold alloy can be heated to anneal or soften it to permit additional working of the material.

As gold is alloyed to reduce its fineness, the hard-

Table 14.1 Various alloys of gold

Alloy	Specific Gravity	Melting Point Fahrenheit	Melting Point Centigrade
Gold 9 K Yellow (UK)	11.2	1641	894
Gold 9 K White (UK)	12.0	1713	934
Gold 10 K White (US)	11.1	1975	1079
Gold 10 K Yellow (US)	11.6	1665	907
Gold 14 K White	12.6	1825	996
Gold 14 K Yellow	13.1	1615	879
Gold 18 K White	14.6	1730	943
Gold 18 K Yellow	15.6	1700	927
Gold 22 K Yellow	17.3	1790	977
Gold 22 K Coin	17.2	1724	940
Fine Gold	19.3	1945	1063

ness increases. Improved hardness, to a degree, is a desirable feature for jewelry that is subject to extensive wear—a ring, for example. The harder material is less subject to scratches and will retain a high polish. By controlling the choice of alloying metals, the color and casting characteristics can be altered.

Of course, lower karat gold is less expensive than pure gold, because the alloy metals are generally less expensive than the gold. Therefore, cost is another reason for producing jewelry using lower karat gold. Because the color of a gold alloy can be manipulated over a range, cost alone is not the only factor that affects personal preferences.

The percentage of gold also affects the desirability of a gold alloy for use in jewelry. 14 K gold is the most common alloy used for fine jewelry in the United States. Although it is considered by most people to be inferior, 10 K gold has improved mechanical characteristics such as hardness and strength. Other cultures, such as in Europe or in the East, insist that fine jewelry should be constructed of 18 K or even 22 K gold in spite of the increased softness and fragility of the finished jewelry. In a final analysis, the customer determines the desirability of the gold fineness.

Gold finer than 14 K is preferred for jewelry outside of the United States.

Over the years the percentage of gold in jewelry has varied somewhat even when the content was specified. For many years stamping jewelry as 14 K implied that it was constructed using an alloy that contained 58 percent gold. Until 1981 the precision with which the alloy was formulated was allowed by law in the United States to vary somewhat. Presumably the allowed tolerance permitted gold solders with less than 58 percent gold to be used while the finished product was still called 14 K gold. Over time it was found that jewelry was often lower in gold content than the specified 58 percent. Debasement, as this is called, dates into ancient history and was often practiced in the manufacture of gold coinage by forgers or unscrupulous governments.

In 1976 the term *plumb gold* was defined to indicate that jewelry differs from the specified fineness by no more than 0.3 percent, not including the solder content. Jewelry items could have fineness no greater than 0.7 percent under the indicated karatage if the solder is included. Gold solders must have the specified fineness to be called plumb.

Gold coinage

Gold and gold coins have been important in commerce since ancient times. Because gold is a relatively scarce commodity, it maintains its value and, in fact, the gold possessed by a country was often the foundation of its currency. Gold and silver were known as "hard" currency and for many years, even in the United States, paper currency could be exchanged for hard currency on demand.

To be used as currency, a coin was expected to contain a precise amount of gold. Some of the earliest coins were composed of electrum, a naturally occurring alloy of gold and silver. When it became possible to produce highly purified gold, coins were manufactured with an alloy precisely formulated with a specified percentage of pure gold plus an alloy metal, usually copper. Pure gold was rarely used for coinage intended for active use, because it is too soft.

Early coins varied in gold content. The gold content of Roman coinage was much more precisely controlled than previously except when official government debasement was practiced by unscrupulous emperors.

For many years the Spanish gold *escudo* was used throughout the world as a standard currency. Gold coinage in denominations of 8, 4, 2, 1, 1/2 and 1/4 *escudo* was commonly minted. The most commonly used coin, 2 escudos, was also known as the *doubloon*. These were originally minted using an alloy that was 92 percent gold (also expressed as 0.92 fine, or 22.08 K).

A silver coinage known as the *real* (pronounced ray-all) was also minted in Spain and in countries that were part of the Spanish empire. The *real* was originally minted from silver that was 0.93 fine. Like the *escudo* it was also minted in denominations of 8, 4, 2, 1, 1/2 and 1/4 *reales*. When an 8-*real* coin was cut in pieces to produce smaller denomination coins, they were known as "pieces-of-eight." If an 8-*real* coin was cut in quarters, each piece was valued at 2 *reales*.

In the early 1930s, the United States, like many other countries, went off the gold standard. That is, paper currency was produced that was not backed by gold bullion stored at Fort Knox, Kentucky. Paper currency could no longer be exchanged for gold or gold coins on demand. In fact, it was made illegal to own gold in the United States except in the form of jewelry. Silver coinage remained in use for many more years in the United States, and then in 1964 even silver alloy coins ceased to be minted.

Gold bullion coins are a convenient way to buy the precious metal.

As of the end of the twentieth century, gold and silver coins were not used as standard currency anywhere in the world. The gold coins that are minted are known as bullion coins and are, in fact, simply a means of transferring a known amount of gold. The value of the coin is determined by the world value of gold, not a denomination stamped on the coin as it was historically. Modern gold coins are generally minted to contain one troy ounce of pure gold (or some specified fraction of an ounce). The actual alloy may differ somewhat in different countries, but generally copper is added to harden the coin. Gold Krugerrands, for example, are 22 K gold. Gold Pandas, minted by the People's Republic of China, are 24 K gold.

The reason for this long discussion is that gold coins may be purchased to make jewelry. This has been a practice of goldsmiths since the dawn of history because gold coins are usually known to contain a prescribed amount of gold. Although the cost of gold bullion coins may vary somewhat depending upon their desirability as a coin, they are an economical source of gold for making jewelry. Bullion coins are conveniently available for purchase containing smaller amounts of gold than standard bullion bars. Later we will discuss the process of alloying bullion coins to make karat gold for jewelry manufacture.

Silver

Silver is available in essentially two alloys: sterling and coin silver. Any metal described by the word silver and another word, such as German silver, actually contains no silver at all. Most jewelry is manufactured from sterling, which is 92.5 percent silver, plus other alloy metals, principally copper. Such jewelry is stamped "Sterling" primarily in the United States, and "925" in much of the rest of the world. Some Mexican jewelers actually make their own sterling by melting together 925 parts pure silver and 75 parts copper.

Some jewelry is made from silver coins and has the composition of coin silver or about 80 percent silver in much of the world. Silver coins in the United States were 90 percent silver. Old Native American jewelry may be constructed of coin silver, because coins were often fabricated into jewelry or were melted for casting.

Purchasing metal for jewelry

There are several sources of precious metal for making jewelry. Because most gold or silver coins are out of general circulation, merely selecting a coin is not possible. Metal for jewelry fabrication is available from all jeweler's suppliers who sell jewelry components, or findings, precious and semi-precious stones, tools, and jewelry-making equipment. It is available in many forms—sheet, wire, bezel material, etc.—for fabrication. Silver is always available as sterling except for bezel material, which is fine silver, because softness is desirable in this case. Gold is available in many finished forms, generally as 10, 14, and 18 karat in the United States. All precious metal is sold based on the daily world market value of the gold or silver content plus a fabrication charge and a profit markup. The markup varies considerably, depending on the quantity of metal purchased, so it is always desirable to purchase precious metal in quantities as large as possible.

Metal for jewelry manufacture is also available from precious metal dealers who specialize in processing and supplying metals only and not the tools and stones sold by the jeweler's suppliers. Metal dealers may offer a slightly better price than jeweler's supply companies; however, the metal is priced to sell in larger quantities. Precious metal dealers also purchase or reprocess scrap or jewelry shop sweepings.

Metal dealers have developed many alloys for casting. Precious metal dealers also experiment and develop special alloys for casting. Dozens of casting alloys are available with different properties. A simple alloy of 92.5 percent silver and 7.5 percent copper is, in fact, sterling, but it may not be as easy to use for lost-wax casting as an alloy that contains some zinc, silicon, or other materials that improve the castability. Of course, all alloys designated as sterling must contain precisely 92.5 percent silver, so the variability is only in the composition of the 7.5 percent alloy material. Some precious metal dealers offer a variety of special deoxidized alloys of silver that cast with a bright surface rather than covered with an oxidation coating that must be removed in a pickling solution.

Gold and silver for casting purposes are generally called casting grain. They are composed of small, more-or-less round beads of metal formed by pouring molten metal into a spray of water. Homemade casting grain may be created by simply cutting up scrap sheet metal or other shapes or by melting the scrap and pouring it into a bucket of water.

Making alloys

There is little merit, economically, in making silver casting grain, although Mexican jewelers are known to do this and roll their own sheet sterling. It is also probably not practical for an individual craftsman to perform the experiments required to develop exactly the right silver casting alloy. Individual alloying of gold, however, is a different matter. Gold jewelry may be constructed of 10 K, 14 K or 18 K gold for various customers. Because this might require a large stock of shapes and casting grain compositions, gold alloying is worth considering. Sometimes it is desirable to alter the karat composition of gold such as making some 10 K casting grain from 14 K grain or scrap.

It is also feasible, and perhaps economical, to stock gold bullion coins that are melted to produce casting grain with various alloy compositions. Krugerrands are currently available with the least markup over their gold content. Precious metal dealers sell "alloy" that is specifically formulated to be added to coins such as the Krugerrand to produce good casting grain of various karat compositions. The only requirement is precise weighing of the alloy. Alloy is available with different characteristics depending on whether it is to be used to produce a cast product or will be used to roll sheets or draw wire. One precious metal dealer lists over 70 alloys for gold alone;

each alloy is designed to be added to 24 K gold to produce a gold alloy with various colors and casting or rolling characteristics.

Scrap gold, pawnshops, testing

Scrap precious metal is always a by-product of jewelry making. Sprues and buttons always remain after casting jewelry, and such scrap is too expensive to be wasted or reprocessed. Whenever a precious-metal alloy is melted, some of the metals with lower melting points vaporize. Consequently, a remelted alloy is never exactly the same composition as the original alloy. Because very small changes in alloy composition may affect the castability of a molten metal, it is generally recommended that scrap be combined with new metal in a 50:50 mixture. This will preserve the casting characteristics of the alloy. When it is not feasible to combine new alloy with scrap, metal dealers provide a special alloy that can be combined in small amounts with scrap metal to restore its desirable casting characteristics. While not specified, these special alloys obviously supply small quantities of various materials that restore the casting characteristics by replacing materials that would be lost during previous processing.

Be careful when using pawn shop gold for casting. Scrap gold may be purchased from pawn shops to use for casting. However, there are certain precautions that must be observed. First, not all gold colored objects with a karat marking are really gold. I have a brass ring marked 14 K that was given to me by a pawn dealer who thought he was buying a gold ring. The safest procedure when buying scrap gold is to invest in a gold testing kit.

Testing to determine whether an object is karat gold can be performed using a kit containing several acids and test pieces of several gold alloys. The object to be tested is scratched across a black stone to leave a gold-colored streak. Another streak is placed next to the test streak using a metal with a known alloy content for reference. Then a drop of test acid of the appropriate concentration for the expected gold content is placed on the two streaks.

Test the quality of scrap gold for casting.

A judgment of the fineness of the gold is then deduced as follows: If the test streak dissolves completely, then the metal is not gold or is a much lower fineness than is indicated. If the test streak dissolves slightly more slowly than the reference streak, the fineness is less than the reference alloy and the test should be repeated with a different reference alloy. If the two streaks remain similar in appearance after applying the test acid, it can be concluded that the test specimen has a gold content very close to the reference metal. Should the test streak appear to dissolve more slowly than reference streak, then a higher gold content is indicated and the next higher karat test metal and acid should be tried in the same way. A gold testing kit does not provide an absolute measure of gold fineness, but it does allow one to identify gold and determine the approximate gold content of an unknown alloy.

In addition to determining the gold content of scrap gold, the quality of the scrap is important when buying the metal for casting. For example, much of the scrap gold chain found in a pawnshop is of little value for casting. Scrap chain often contains a solder core or many solder joints that make it a poor choice for casting. Chains with large individually soldered links may be satisfactory, and at one time heavy chain links were used as currency.

The best choices of scrap gold for jewelry making are wedding bands. Bands may be solid gold or they may contain a single solder joint of non-plumb solder that can be cut out to make high-quality karat scrap that will cast reasonably well, especially if combined with new casting grain. Other scrap rings may contain numerous solder joints that make them less desirable for casting.

Platinum and other metals

Several metals in the platinum group are of some importance in jewelry manufacture. Rhodium is used predominantly for plating gold or silver jewelry to produce a lustrous and hard finish. Palladium is alloyed with gold to make so-called white gold. On the other hand, pure platinum is used to make precious jewelry. At one time platinum was considered much more valuable than gold; however, its current market price per ounce is not too different from the price of gold. On the other hand, platinum is commonly used as 100 percent platinum rather than as an alloy; consequently, the finished value of a piece of platinum jewelry may be higher. Platinum melts at almost twice the temperature of the common gold alloys; therefore, special casting procedures are required. In particular, a special high-temperature platinum investment is required, and the casting centrifuges are constructed somewhat differently to produce higher accelerations and greater casting forces.

Homemade Equipment

Overview

Throughout this book we have mentioned home-made or inexpensive equipment that can be used in place of some of the more expensive items. Some of these suggestions require little elaboration; however, this chapter will provide further details and some "how-to" instructions. The big-ticket items used in lost-wax casting are the vacuum system, the burnout oven, a centrifuge, and perhaps a melting torch.

Some relatively expensive items, such as a good beam balance for weighing wax models and investment, may be obtained from inexpensive sources. I purchased a good triple-beam balance at a flea market for a fraction of its original price. Some local sheriff's offices or police departments may be willing to dispose of quality balances that were confiscated in drug arrests if they are convinced that the new use is legitimate.

Before showing some homemade pieces of equipment, it might be useful to examine the commercial
equivalents that we wish to copy. Figure 15.1 shows
an inexpensive vacuum table that can be used as a
starting point. Previously we have shown inte-
grated vacuum systems while this illustration
shows the vacuum table as a separate component
that can be combined with any suitable vacuum
pump. The vacuum table may be used either for
debubblizing using the bell jar, or the bell jar can be
set aside and the black rubber pad can be changed
to a red high-temperature silicon-rubber pad for
casting. We will consider less expensive or homemade parts for the separate components.

Vacuum pumps

A vacuum pump is an essential equipment item for
a shop that will be used for other than an occasional
casting project. We have pointed out how it is used
both for removing air bubbles from a liquid investment mixture and for vacuum-assisted casting.
Standard high-vacuum pumps similar to the one

shown in Figure 15.2 may be obtained from a number of scientific salvage companies; however, it is also possible to make a vacuum pump from some rather improbable objects.

A refrigeration compressor makes a good vacuum pump.

An air-conditioning or refrigeration compressor can be used as a vacuum pump. Practically any automobile air conditioner compressor can be attached to an electric motor and used for removing bubbles from investment or vacuum-assisted casting. These may be obtained from automobile salvage yards for a modest price. The older models are easier to mount and attach to an electric motor than the newer rotary units. All automotive air conditioner compressors have an electric clutch attached to the automobile engine with a drive belt that is used to activate the compressor. It is necessary to get someone to weld or braze the clutch assembly together so that it is permanently actuated. The compressor may then be attached to an electric motor using the

**Figure 15.3
Manual vacuum pump
constructed from a
plumber's helper**

pulley that is part of the clutch assembly. When
first turned on, determine which pipe or compressor
fitting is intake suction and attach a hose from that
connection to a vacuum table. Attach an automotive
fuel-line filter to the output connection to trap the
lubricating oil in the pump rather than spraying it
out into the air.

There are other methods of obtaining a vacuum for
vacuum-assisted casting. While not suitable for
removing air bubbles from investment, a manual
pump similar to the one shown in Figure 15.3 will
provide adequate suction for casting. Suitable
pumps are sold as a plumber's helper or as a high-
volume pump for inflating rubber boats or beach
toys. These may be attached to a commercial vacuum table or the homemade unit made from scraps
of wood shown in Figure 15.4.

Figure 15.4
Homemade vacuum
table for vacuum-
assisted casting.

The vacuum table for casting is made from a block of wood with a gasket of high-temperature silicon-rubber cemented to the block. Drill intersecting holes from the hole in the rubber gasket to the side of the wooden block. Seal the wood in the passageway with some paint or varnish, and screw a pipe or hose fitting into the wooden block. An inexpensive fuel filter in the line between the vacuum table and the vacuum pump will prevent any investment from entering the pump.

A similar vacuum table can be constructed from a piece of wood or metal large enough to permit the use of a vacuum bell for debubblizing. A commercial bell jar is relatively expensive and can be replaced with a piece of large diameter PVC pipe with a piece of heavy glass cemented to the top so that the contents may be observed when liquid investment is vacuumed. With a little ingenuity and talent with tools, a $500 vacuum system can be replaced with homemade substitutes for less than $50.

Steam dewaxers

The usual steam dewaxer purchased from a jeweler's supply company will cost several hundred dollars. Qualitatively, all that is needed is an electrically heated pot that will generate steam and a tray or other support that will permit the sprue-down flasks to be exposed to hot steam while remaining above the water in the pot. An inexpensive rice or vegetable steamer immediately comes to mind. An electric frying pan with a wire shelf to support the flasks will also work. Any thing from the local Goodwill Store that will boil water to make steam is worth trying.

Burnout ovens

The burnout oven is another costly piece of equipment that can be replaced with less expensive substitutes. Some persons have performed burnout with a torch or a gas burner, but more satisfactory alternatives can be made.

We have pointed out earlier that a complete burnout may be achieved using charcoal. This is suitable for an occasional burnout, but most of a bag of charcoal briquettes is required to burn out one flask. A convenient way to use charcoal for burnout is to obtain a device for starting charcoal in a grill such as shown in Figure 15.5. Place the flask on the shelf inside and fill the metal column with briquettes. Add charcoal starter fluid, ignite, and add more charcoal as needed until the burnout is completed in about two hours.

A small burnout oven can be constructed from two lightweight insulating firebricks and a length of heating-element wire. The soft firebrick is cut into

**Figure 15.5
Charcoal starter unit
that may be used to
burnout a flask or two.**

four pieces that are held together with a band of
metal and are set on another half brick. Grooves can
be gouged into the firebrick with a screwdriver, and
a length of coiled resistance wire is pressed into the
grooves. A completed furnace suitable for single-
flask burnout is shown in Figure 15.6. The furnace

**Figure 15.6
Small burnout furnace
constructed by
splitting two soft
firebricks and adding
a resistance heating
element.**

is closed simply by placing another firebrick over the opening on top.

The heating element for the furnace should be suitable for operation on standard 120-volt house electric circuits in North America or 240 volts in other parts of the world. Coiled heating elements may be obtained from salvage dealers, electrical suppliers, or by removing heating elements with the proper voltage rating from electric heaters of various sorts. A readily available source of resistance wire is a 120-volt heating element designed for a motor home water heater.

If the heating element has a power rating of 600 watts or less, a conventional wall light-dimmer switch may be used as an oven controller. A higher wattage electric oven controller, sometimes called a "continuous switch", may be obtained at a higher price from an electrical parts distributor or pottery-kiln manufacturer. For high-temperature burnout, as described earlier, all that is required is to determine the controller setting necessary to maintain approximately 1350° F in the small furnace.

Centrifuges

If one prefers centrifugal to vacuum casting, some sort of centrifuge is required to swing the flask in a circle and force metal into the mold. For persons with plenty of nerve, the method first used by dentists to swing the flask is inexpensive. A simple metal sling to hold the flask on the end of a chain may be used to swing the flask in a circle over one's head. The parts required and the appropriate motion is shown on Page 97 of *The Complete Metalsmith,* by Tim McCreight, Revised Edition, 1991.

A number of homemade centrifuges have been proposed and some construction diagrams have been circulated on the Internet. Rather than constructing a broken-arm centrifuge the simplest mechanical design is a straight arm mounted on an electric motor. Another hand-powered design rotates the centrifuge arm using a mechanism similar to the rope starter used on some small gasoline engines. Some metalworking skill is necessary to construct a sturdy mechanism that will not fly apart when experiencing the high acceleration rates required for effective centrifugal casting.

If all else fails, make the rounds of the older dentists in your area and try to bargain for the centrifugal casting machine they have stored in a closet. Many dentists purchased casting equipment years ago, but for economic reasons most of them currently send their gold inlay and crown casting jobs to dental laboratories.

Steam casters

A steam-casting unit is simply a handle with a cup-shaped device for holding a number of layers of moist paper. I described one in Chapter 10 made with a jar cap attached to an old wooden tool handle or a short section of wooden dowel. The jar top tends to be somewhat flexible, but a sturdier tool can be constructed from a 2- to 4-inch galvanized pipe cap. The internal threads also help to keep the layers of paper from falling out of the cap.

More inexpensive equipment

Elsewhere we have mentioned several alternatives to "store-bought" equipment specifically designed for the jewelry trade. For example, tin cans will work as flasks although a single burnout is usually sufficient to burn almost through the thin metal used in modern tin cans. Be sure not to use aluminum cans that will melt at the temperatures used for burnout.

A better choice for flasks are sections of 2-inch exhaust pipe that may be obtained for little or no cost at local muffler shops. Exhaust pipes are often cut to fit a particular automobile and there is usually a pile of cut-off pieces somewhere in the shop. Cut into 2-1/2 inch sections, the exhaust pipe looks just like the flasks purchased from a jeweler's supplier. Some pipe sections I have obtained are not stainless steel and tend to rust after being used. There are also some exhaust pipe couplers available in auto-parts stores that will work.

A number of other useful items can be purchased locally. Kitchen tongs for handling hot flasks may be purchased at most outlet stores for a fraction of the cost of flask tongs available from jewelry suppliers. Instead of spatulas from the trade sources, pick up an icing spatula from the kitchenware department.

Your local welding shop will be able to provide a number of useful items. They can obtain any torch or torch accessory at a fraction of the jewelry-supply cost. Also pick up a pair of long welder's leather gloves. Welder's gloves are not thermally insulated, but they will protect you from splattering metal and will allow you to let go of a hot flask before it really burns you.

If you want to try burnout over a flame instead of using a burnout oven, inexpensive propane cookers are available at various hunting supply shops. This is also a good source of vibrating tumblers, which are used by ammunition reloaders to polish brass cartridge cases. The price is about half the cost for the identical piece of equipment sold for jewelry-making purposes.

A little scrounging and some mechanical skill is all that is needed to get started in the craft of lost-wax casting. Even professional jewelers may ask their dentists for their worn out dental tools for reshaping into wax-welding tools.

16

A Final Word

This book has just scratched the surface of a topic that can become an exciting hobby or a fascinating professional career. There are many directions to go from the basic material presented here.

With the simple techniques that were presented in Chapter 4, one can immediately proceed to designing original wax models using wax wire and sheet wax. After a few minutes instruction, my teenage daughter produced several ring designs.

Molds for reproducing designs are easy to make using Silastic® RTV rubber. *RTV* stands for "room temperature vulcanizing," and inexpensive kits are available that can be used to produce silicon rubber molds. Then a manually-operated wax pot is all that is needed to start your own production line.

Help from other more experienced casters and jewelry makers is as near as your computer and the Internet. Simply go to www.yahoogroups.com and follow a link to "Hobbies and Crafts." Further links will lead to a list of over 250 groups that specialize in "Jewelry Making." Several groups are specifically dedicated to lost-wax casting. Sign up for a couple of groups and you will immediately be connected by email with hundreds of other persons with interests similar to yours. Any email you submit to the "list-server" will be forwarded to all of the group members. Introduce yourself as a "Newbie" to the list members, and help on just about any question will be on its way to you by return email. Don't neglect this valuable resource. You may find yourself communicating with professional jewelers or owners of the companies that provide the lost-wax casting tools and supplies.

The Internet is an invaluable resource for both new and experienced lost-wax casters. Many of the tool, equipment, and supply dealers have Internet sites where you can obtain technical information, as well as order tools and supplies. With a credit card, practically anything you need can be ordered and shipped to your doorstep.

It is my hope that this book has opened the craft of lost-wax casting for you. As a hobby it does not need to be expensive. For the serious craftsperson, we hope some useful information has been provided to aid in setting up your shop.

You may contact the author by Email at the following address:

fredsias@woodsmerepress.com

Glossary

Agora - The gathering place or market place in ancient Greece.

Alloy - A substance, usually of two or more metals, that are intimately mixed together by melting.

Anneal - Heat treatment of a metal to relieve internal stresses and make it soft to permit further cold working. This is done by quenching gold and silver.

Ashanti casting - A primitive lost-wax casting method still used by craftsmen in Ghana.

Avoirdupois - The weight system that includes pounds and ounces.

Beeswax - The natural wax obtained from bee hives, which was used in early or primitive forms of lost-wax casting.

Bezel - A piece of metal used to surround a gem stone or cabochon to hold it in place on a ring or other piece of jewelry.

Bezel setting - A gem stone or cabochon set in a piece of jewelry using a bezel in contrast to prongs.

Bezel wax - A wax wire shaped to use for forming bezels in wax models used for lost-wax casting.

Brass - An alloy composed primarily of copper and zinc.

Broken-arm casting machine - A form of centrifugal casting machine where the flask and crucible are initially set at right angles to the casting arm. See straight-arm machine.

Bronze - An alloy composed primarily of copper and tin.

Buff - Short for buffing wheel. A cloth or leather wheel attached to a motor to be used for finishing and polishing metal objects.

Bullion Coins - Coins made containing a precise amount of precious metal that are struck primarily for metallic content rather than as currency.

Burnout - The process of eliminating all wax from a mold in the lost-wax casting process.

Button - A small quantity of metal remaining in the pouring cup of a mold after the metal hardens.

Cabochon - A polished, dome-shaped gemstone.

Carbon dioxide - An odorless, colorless gas that forms when carbon chemically reacts with oxygen.

Carat - A weight measure (200 mg) for gemstones. There are 5 carats to a gram. See also Karat.

Casting grain - Casting metal that has been formed into small particles or beads for ease in weighing and melting.

Centrifugal casting - A lost-wax casting technique that uses centrifugal force to inject metal into an investment mold.

Centrifugal force - An outward force on a body rotating about an axis.

Centrifuge - Another name for a centrifugal casting machine.

Ceramic-shell casting - A modern form of lost-wax casting whereby the mold is made of a thin ceramic shell rather than a massive block of investment.

Chaplets - Small metal pins used to hold a mold core in position after the wax model has been eliminated by heating.

Cire perdue - Another name for the lost-wax casting process.

Core - Material that is enclosed within a wax model of an object that will be hollow when cast.

Crucible - A ceramic or refractory container for melting metal.

Double boiler - A double cooking utensil where a bottom pot containing water is used to heat an upper pot with steam.

Electrum - A naturally occurring alloy composed primarily of gold and silver.

File card - A brush with metal bristles used to clean metal or wax shavings from a file.

File, double-cut - A file with teeth cut in two directions to remove metal faster.

File, single-cut - A file with teeth cut in only one direction.

Fillet - A foundry term that refers to a rounding of internal angles where two wax or metal surfaces come together.

Firebricks - Bricks made of refractory material to be able to withstand high temperature.

Firing - The process of raising clay to a high temperature to cause it to become a ceramic object.

Flask - The metal tube or other container in which an investment mold is made.

Flexible-shaft tool - A motor-driven tool used to shape and finish jewelry.

Flux - A chemical, usually borax, that scavenges impurities from molten metal. It also protects the molten metal from oxidizing. The term is also used for a variety of substances, including borax, that are used to protect heated metal from oxidation and facilitate soldering.

Founder - A metalsmith who works in a foundry and casts metal objects.

Foundry - A shop or area used for casting metal objects.

Gate - A passageway in a mold through which metal passes into a mold cavity.

Gesso - A historical name for plaster of Paris.

Gloss over - A term sometimes used to describe the change in surface appearance from glossy to matte when investment hardens in a flask.

Goldsmith - The traditional name for a metalsmith that makes articles for adornment. (See Silversmith.)

Grain - A unit of weight measure. Also the name for small pellets of metal used for casting.

Gram - A measure of weight in the metric system.

Gravity casting - Any form of casting where the force of gravity is the only force used to inject metal into the mold.

Green strength - A term used in ceramics to describe the strength of a clay object after air-drying but not fired.

Gypsum - The mineral material from which plaster of Paris and low-temperature investment is made.

Invest - Foundry definition: the process of enclosing a wax model or tree inside of liquid investment that will harden to form a mold.

Investment - The foundry definition of material that is used to make a mold for lost-wax casting.

Jeweler's bronze - A casting metal, primarily of copper and tin, used to simulate gold for jewelry samples.

Karat - A measure of the gold content of gold alloys. 24 karats is pure gold.

Lost-wax process - A casting process whereby a model is made of wax that is then melted out of the mold before injecting metal into the mold.

Mass finishing methods - Techniques for cleaning, smoothing, and polishing jewelry using vibrating tumblers.

Microcrystalline wax - A form of wax that is a by-product of the petroleum industry that remains after the volatile portions have been removed from oil.

Milliliter - A measure of fluid volume in the metric system. It is equivalent to a cubic centimeter.

Paraffin - A brittle wax obtained from petroleum.

Peening - A process of hardening metal by striking it with a hammer.

Pennyweight - A unit of weight used for measuring precious metals.

Perforated flask - A casting flask that has been perforated with many holes to reduce the resistance to air escaping from a mold. It may be used for centrifugal or vacuum casting with the appropriate equipment.

Pickling solution - A solution of hot acid used to remove oxides and sulfides from the surface of cast objects.

Plumb gold - Gold that is alloyed to precise specifications.

Polyethylene - A plastic that is also obtained from petroleum.

Porosity - When used in the casting sense this word refers to small pits that appear on parts of a casting due to a large variety of improper casting procedures. The word is also used to refer to the state of being full of pores and permeable to air and gases.

Pouring cup - The funnel-shaped opening into a mold through which metal is poured or injected.

Prong setting - A setting for gem stones whereby the stone is held in place with prongs that are bent over the stone.

PVC tubing - An inexpensive polyvinyl plastic tubing used for plumbing.

Refractory A non-metallic material that is capable of withstanding very high temperatures.

Refractory cement - A cement used for making furnaces and able to withstand high temperatures.

Ring - A term used by dental technicians to describe the metal reinforcement around an investment mold. Also called a flask.

Ring head - The design part of a ring that may consist of metal designs and a gem stone or stones. See ring shank.

Ring shank - The part of a finger ring that encircles the finger. See ring head.

Riser - A cavity in a mold that is not part of the object being cast but is present to supply molten metal to the casting as it shrinks while hardening.

Rolling mill - A machine consisting of two adjustable rollers that can be used to reduce the thickness of metal.

Rouge - A red iron-oxide polishing compound.

Shot peening - The process of hardening and polishing metal objects by placing them in a vibrating or rotary tumbler full of steel shot.

Silicon dioxide - A constituent of many investments. Sand, quartz.

Silicon rubber - A special form of rubber, usually red, that is able to withstand high temperatures.

Silversmith - The traditional name for a metalsmith that makes utensils such as flatware, plates, tumblers, etc. Also used less precisely as a name for someone that makes things of silver. Also see Goldsmith.

Solder - Any material, usually a metal alloy, that may be melted and used to join together two objects without melting them.

Sprue - A passageway in the mold through which air or metal may pass. Also the process of attaching wax sprue wires to a model that will be enclosed in investment to form a lost-wax mold.

Sprue wax - Wax rods or wires with a low melting point designed to form the sprue passageways in a lost-wax mold.

Steam casting - A variety of lost-wax casting where steam pressure is used to force metal into a mold.

Sticky wax - A tan wax formed in chunks, rods, or in tins that is used as a cement for joining other pieces of wax used in the lost-wax process.

Straight-arm casting machine - A form of centrifugal casting machine where the flask, crucible, and casting arm are all in a straight line. See broken-arm machine.

Tree - A structure composed of many wax models attached to a wax trunk that is enclosed in investment to improve the productivity of the lost-wax process.

Tripoli - A dark brown compound used to cut and finish metal prior to final polishing.

Troy - A system of weights used with precious metals.

Troy ounce - A measure of weight that is equivalent to approximately 31.1 grams.

Tumbler - A rotary or vibrating device used for polishing stones or metal objects by tumbling.

Turbo torch - A form of acetylene torch for melting that causes air to swirl and thereby increases the flame temperature.

Vacuum-assisted casting - A lost-wax casting technique that employs a vacuum pump to remove air and gases from a mold so that atmospheric pressure can force metal into the mold cavities.

Vent - A passageway in a mold through which air and gases can escape from the mold cavity.

Vibrating tumbler - A machine used for polishing stones or metal that uses vibration to cause the contents to roll and tumble.

Water streaking - A surface blemish formed on cast objects when investment is poured too soon and is allowed to sit for some time before hardening.

White gold - A gold alloy containing nickel or palladium to give it a white silvery appearance.

Work harden - The property of certain metals such as sterling and alloy gold that hardens the metal when repeatedly bent or struck.

Appendix A

To change From	To	Multiply By
Cubic Centimeters	Ounces, Fluid	0.0338
Grains, Troy	Grams	0.0648
Grains, Troy	Milligrams	64.8
Grains, Troy	Ounces, Avoir.	0.00229
Grains, Troy	Ounces, Troy	0.0021
Grains, Troy	Pennyweights (dwts)	0.0417
Grams	Carats	5
Grams	Grains	15.4324
Grams	Pennyweights (dwts)	0.64301
Grams	Ounces, Troy	0.03215
Inches	Centimeters	2.54001
Inches	Millimeters	25.4
Kilograms	Ounces, Troy	32.1507
Kilograms	Pounds, Avoir.	2.2046
Liters	Quarts (Liquid)	1.06
Ounces, Troy	Pennyweights (dwts)	20
Ounces, Troy	Grams	31.1035
Ounces, Fluid	Cubic Centimeters	29.5737
Pennyweights (dwts)	Grains	24
Pennyweights (dwts)	Grams	1.5552
Pennyweights (dwts)	Ounces, Troy	0.05
Quarts	Liters	0.94633

Appendix B

Typical Burnout Profiles
(Notes from Swest, Inc.)

The following burnout profiles are suggested for wax elimination. (See note 1)
Select the proper burnout profile according to the size of the flasks.

5-hour burnout	8-hour burnout	12-hour burnout
For flasks up to 2-1/2" x 2-1/2 "	For flasks up to 3-1/2" x 4"	For flasks up to 4" x 8"
Preheat furnace To 300° F (149° C)	Preheat furnace To 300° F (149° C)	Preheat furnace To 300° F (149° C)
1 hour -- 300° F (149° C)	2 hours -- 300° F (149° C)	2 hours -- 300° F (149° C)
1 hour -- 700° F (371° C)	2 hours -- 700° F (371° C)	2 hours -- 600° F (316° C)
2 hours -- 1350° F (732° C)	3 hours -- 1350° F (732° C)	2 hours -- 900° F (482° C)
1 hour -- See note 2	1 hour -- See note 2	4 hours -- 1350° F (732° C)
		2 hours -- See note 2

Note 1: Check instructions provided with the investment you purchase for recommended burnout schedules.
Note 2: During the last hour of burnout the temperature should be adjusted so that the flasks are at the correct temperature for casting when removed from the oven. See Appendix D.
Examples:
> Mold temperature for ladies' rings or lacy items should be 900° F (482° C) to 1000° F (538° C).
> Mold temperature for men's rings or heavier designs should be 700° F (371°C) to 900° F (482° C).

Appendix C

Investment Mixing Chart

To determine investment and water requirement for various size flasks.

Flask Diameter	Height of Flask							
	2"	2-1/2"	3"	3-1/2"	4"	5"	6"	7"
2"	150 g / 60 ml	175 g / 70 ml	200 g / 80 ml	250 g / 100 ml	300 g / 120 ml	350 g / 140 ml		
2-1/2"	225 g / 90 ml	300 g / 120 ml	350 g / 140 ml	400 g / 160 ml	450 g / 180 ml	575 g / 230 ml		
3"	350 g / 140 ml	425 g / 170 ml	500 g / 200 ml	600 g / 240 ml	700 g / 280 ml	850 g / 340 ml	1025 g / 410 ml	1250 g / 500 ml
3-1/2"	450 g / 180 ml	575 g / 230 ml	675 g / 270 ml	800 g / 320 ml	900 g / 360 ml	1150 g / 460 ml	1375 g / 550 ml	1600 g / 640 ml
4"	500 g / 200 ml	650 g / 260 ml	750 g / 300 ml	900 g / 360 ml	1150 g / 460 ml	1375 g / 550 ml	1600 g / 640 ml	1825 g / 730 ml
5"					1700 g / 680 ml	2150 g / 860 ml	2500 g / 1000 ml	2975 g / 1190 ml

- *NOTE*: When calculating the volume of investment for each flask size, the amount of water is set to the nearest 10 ml to simplify and improve the precision of the fluid measurement.
- Calculations are for a 40/100 mixing ratio and a working time of 9 minutes.

Appendix D
Jewelry Alloy Casting Properties[1]

Alloy[2]	Appromate Melting Temp.[3] (°F)	Appromate Melting Temp.[3] (°C)	Ratio of Metal To Wax	Flask Casting Temp.[4] (°F)	Flask Casting Temp.[4] (°C)
Silver (Fine)	1762	962	10.5 : 1	1300	704
Silver (Sterling)	1640	893	10.5 : 1	1200	649
Gold 9 K Y (UK)	1641	894	11.2 : 1	1200	649
Gold 10 K Y (US)	1665	907	11.6 : 1	1200	649
Gold 14 K Y	1615	879	13 : 1	1200	649
Gold 18 K Y	1700	927	16 : 1	1200	649
Gold 22 K Y	1790	977	17.7 : 1	1325	718
Gold 24 K	1945	1064	19.3 : 1	1350	732
Gold 9 K W (UK)	1713	934	12 : 1	1300	704
Gold 10 K W (US)	1925	1052	13 : 1	1300	704
Gold 14 K W	1825	996	12.6 : 1	1300	704
Gold 18 K W	1730	943	14.6 : 1	1300	704
Beryllium Copper	1800	982	8 : 1	800	427
Platinum	3224	1773	22 : 1	1600	871
Aluminum	1200	649	2.7 : 1	400	204
White Bronze	1550	843	8 : 1	900	482
Silicon Bronze	1780	971	8.5 : 1	900	482
Pewter	585	307	8 : 1	Ambient	Ambient

Notes:

1. Selected representative alloys.

2. Value for a specific alloy. Alloy composition and properties can vary.

3. Alloys become more fluid over a range of temperatures. This is an average temperature when the melt is very fluid.

4. Approximate upper limit of temperature for **vacuum casting light-weight objects** using a six-inch flask. Heavy weight objects may be cast with a flask temperature up to 150° F (66° C) lower. Flask casting temperature may reduced further for smaller flasks or increased for larger flasks. Flask casting temperature may be further reduced when using centrifugal casting equipment. Use refiner's recommendation for specific alloys.

Appendix E

CASTING PROBLEM TROUBLESHOOTING

Problem	Possible Cause
Porosity (or small pits in metal)	Inadequate sprues or gates
	Sprue too small
	Inadequate riser
	Inadequate button
	Melting metal with oxidizing flame
	Models too close together in a tree
	Flask too hot
	Sulphur compounds from investment in inadequately cleaned reused sprues
	Baby powder used for mold release
	Burnout above 1450° F
	Mixture of large and small casting sizes
	Burnout time too short
	Inadequate oxygen during burnout
	Model made of the harder waxes
	Model made of plastic
	Flame too high in gas burnout oven
	Oven exhaust vent restriction
	Overpacking oven
	Severe metal overheating
	Overuse of metal (without replenishment)
	Use of centrifugal casting machine
Hot tears	Poorly designed model
	Too fast solidification
	Flask too hot
	Metal too hot
	Location on tree
	Alloy characteristics
	Use of rectangular gates
	Model too close to button

Problem	Possible Cause
Cracks in casting	Too rapid cooling
	Quenching too soon
	Investment too hard (too little water)
	Boric acid additive in investment when used with deoxidized alloys
	Acid divestment of silicon alloys
	Alloy contamination
	Gate too small
Brittleness	Apparent brittleness probably cracks
Foreign particles	Too much water in investment
	Sharp corners on model
	No fillets at sprue junctions
	Improperly fluxed crucible
	Inadequate burnout
	Metal particles in wax
Incomplete casting	Casting metal not hot enough
	Flask too cool
	Inadequate burnout (too short)
	Inadequate vacuum
	Leaks in vacuum system
	Poor seal between flask and machine
	Vacuum line filters clogged
	Flask needed additional air passageways
	Centrifugal machine not wound enough
	Sprues or gates too small
Fins on casting	Cracked investment from over drying
	Excessive drying on weekend
Sulfur dioxide buildup	Burnout above 1450° F
	Insufficient oxygen supply
	Overpacking oven
	Oven exhaust restriction
	Backdraft or lack of exhaust
	Severe overheating of metal
	Investment powder in remelt
Water streaking	Investing mold too soon so that water collects on model surface before the investment hardens

Index

Made in United States
Troutdale, OR
04/22/2024

19362498R00120